Giving Back to the Earth

A Teacher's Guide to *Project Puffin* and Other Seabird Studies

Giving Back to the Earth

A Teacher's Guide to *Project Puffin* and Other Seabird Studies

Pete Salmansohn and
Stephen W. Kress

Illustrations by Lucy Gagliardo

A National Audubon Society Book

Tilbury House, Publishers
Gardiner, Maine

Fitzhenry & Whiteside Publishers
Markham, Ontario, Canada

Tilbury House, Publishers
132 Water Street
Gardiner, ME 04345

Published in Canada by
Fitzhenry & Whiteside
195 Allstate Parkway
Markham, ON, L3R 4T8

First Edition, March 1997.

10 9 8 7 6 5 4 3 2 1

Library of Congress Cataloging-in-Publication Data

Salmansohn, Pete.
Giving back to the earth : a teacher's guide to *Project Puffin* and other seabird studies / by Pete Salmansohn and. Stephen W. Kress.
p. cm.
"A National Audubon Society book."
Includes bibliographical references.
ISBN 0-88448-172-7 (alk. paper)
1. Wildlife conservation—Study and teaching—Activity programs. 2. Wildlife reintroduction—Study and teaching—Activity programs. 3. Atlantic puffin—Maine. I. Kress, Stephen II. Title
QL83.15.K74 1997
372.3'57—dc 20 95-47795
CIP

Canadian Cataloging-in-Publication Data

Salamansohn, Pete, 1947–
Giving back to the Earth : a teacher's guide to Project Puffin
Includes bibliographical references.
ISBN 1--55041-284-1
1. Wildlife reintroduction--Study and teaching--Activity programs. 2. Atlantic puffin--Study and teaching--Activity programs. II. Kress, Stephen W. II. Title.
QL83.15.S25 1997 372.3'57 C97-900054-8

Cover Design: Susan Sherman, Ars Agassiz, Cambridge, MA
Text Design and Layout: Nina Medina, Basil Hill Graphics, Somerville, ME
Editorial/Production: Jennifer Elliott, Ruth LaChance
Marketing: Michelle Gifford
Office: Jolene Collins
Warehouse: William Hoch
Printing and Binding: Bookcrafters, Fredericksburg, VA

To Ellen Eberhart (1950–1995). A gifted educator, a brave and loving human being. Her teaching and life sparkled with an exuberant sense of wonder.

Contents

Acknowledgements

Any honest author of a guide such as this must admit a great indebtedness to the unnamed pioneers of environmental education who devised many creative activities a long time ago. For example, who was it who came up with the first version of the bird beak game, or with using a ball of twine and twenty kids to build a food web? To those folks, we are grateful.

We want to thank Mark Melnicove who first suggested this book as a companion to *Project Puffin*, and to Jennifer Elliott, Michelle Gifford, and Jolene Collins at Tilbury House for making this a reality.

Lucy Gagliardo was exceptionally patient and reasonable while we continued to make demands for more and more artwork. Her care and skill have taken this book a lot further than we originally imagined.

We thank Melanie Walker for her savvy sense of elementary school art projects and materials, and for creating the puffin puppet and template, as well as the quilt and wall-hanging directions. Ted Gilman generously supplied his activities on watching gulls, bird behaviors, and waterbirds. Thanks to Loretta Jones for providing the activity on how seabirds manage to stay warm while living in a cold ocean. Thanks to Joan Kaye for getting us started with art projects in the first place, to Susan Schubel for turning an ordinary envelope into a flying puffin, and to Kathy Barrett at the Lawrence Hall of Science for advice in adapting an OBIS activity. Jim Booker, Maine coast artist and marine educator extraordinaire, donated his original design and plans for the puffin model. The folks at the Environmental Schools in Ocean Park, Maine, and the librarian at the Maine Audubon Society gave us some good ideas for hands-on games. Margaret Barker and Martha Fischer, both of the Cornell Lab of Ornithology, offered materials and comments on Project PigeonWatch and Project FeederWatch. Our thanks to Steve Van Matre's Sunship Earth Program for the idea of an environmental pledge.

Mary Gunther at the Baltimore Aquarium furnished the list of zoos and aquariums in Canada and U.S. that display live puffins. Thanks also to Marcia Jaquith, Pat Torpey, Meryl Sundove, Donna Ramil, Rose Borzik, Beth Huning, Brad Allen, Craig Newberger, Jo Haney, Joe Gray, and the kind staff at the Skidompha Library in Damariscotta, Maine.

We'd like to extend a special thanks to Katherine Santone, Audubon's licensing director, for her efforts in making this book, and *Project Puffin*, official National Audubon Society publications.

When the animals come to us,
asking for our help,
will we know what they are saying?
When the plants speak to us
in their delicate, beautiful language,
will we be able to answer them?
When the planet herself
sings to us in our dreams,
will we be able to wake ourselves and act?

—Gary Lawless
First Sight of Land
Blackberry Books, 1990

Introduction

This is a book of hope and optimism. Its simple philosophy—giving back to the earth—is the same mission that has guided our twenty-three-year effort to restore puffins and other seabirds to the Maine coast. We saw a biological and aesthetic void caused by centuries of exploitation, and we sought to fill it.

Our goal within these pages is to help you—the educator or parent—help your children appreciate and understand the wondrous world of puffins, seabirds, and the ocean. Children are natural allies with things wild and winged, and they're just waiting for more opportunities to learn.

Because this book is designed for grades three to six, we may be straddling two different worlds, separated by differences in the developmental stages of the children you may be working with. Our experience, and recent research (Sobel*), strongly suggests that younger children, perhaps up to grade four or beyond, need the time and opportunity to enjoy nature, to play in it, to make believe they're birds or whales, to write stories and sing songs, and, most importantly, to develop emotional empathy for animals and plants. Fifth and sixth graders, however, are beginning to look beyond home and school to a larger world and can usually start considering issues of social responsibility. (They too, of course, need plenty of time for exploration, empathy, and play.)

The last thing a concerned adult wants to do is to give children a sense of powerlessness or pessimism. For the older students, then, local initiatives where they can readily see the fruits of their labors are heartily recommended over studying the perplexing state of global ecology. An awareness of environmental history and current human impacts on the sea is necessary for an understanding of the puffin's world, but we suggest treading lightly.

The activities that follow are organized around seven major themes derived from the companion book, *Project Puffin*. These themes range from the power and creativity of one's "dreams," to understanding how puffins survive a life at sea, to protecting and enhancing habitat for wildlife. Activities include art projects, writing, science, graphing skills, mathematics, role playing, and just plain play. It's a mixed-media approach, designed to interest and motivate through a variety of learning styles.

Puffins are a great animal for educators to use as a focal point for their lessons because they're so cute. Their appealing nature quickly brings in learners of all stripes and allows the facilitator to explore a variety of topics. Enjoy. And remember, giving children the opportunity to love nature is probably the greatest thing we adults can do in our own "giving back to the earth."

* Sobel, David. "Beyond Ecophobia: Reclaiming the Heart in Nature Education." *Orion* magazine, Autumn 1995.

A Note to Educators: Seabirds vs. Landbirds

Our focus in these pages is mainly on puffins and other birds associated with the northern oceans. As you read through the book you'll see that many, if not all of the activities specifically involving seabirds and how they live, are adaptable to the study of landbirds. For educators interested in teaching a larger unit on birds in general, there are a number of good activity guides (see the bibliographies for Themes I and VI) that focus more on landbirds such as sparrows, pigeons, robins, etc.

But seabirds and landbirds are more alike than they are different. It's the adaptations that birds have evolved over eons of time to successfully live either a maritime or terrestrial existence that constitute the principal differences. For example, a puffin's breastbones are dense and quite flattened to provide resistance to water pressure at depths which may surpass 100 feet. This anatomical adaptation protects the bird's internal organs. A robin's bone structure is hollower, differently shaped, and weaker, but is perfectly fine for the non-watery existence it leads. Puffins and robins are among the more than 7,000 known species of birds, and each species is wonderfully adapted to its own special habitat.

What Is a Puffin?

Puffins are small diving seabirds that live in the cold ocean waters of the northern hemisphere. They're members of the *auk* or *alcid* family of birds, a group comprised of twenty-two living species. Auks are generally black above and white below (for camouflage), swim after small fish and crustaceans, and usually nest in colonies. They stand upright and have a largish head, a short tail, and a plump body. Auks resemble penguins—their southern ecological counterparts—but penguins are flightless and modern-day auks are not.

The Great Auk was the largest member of the family, standing about two feet high, but was hunted to extinction by 1834. Living members of the group include guillemots, murres, razorbills, murrelets, and auklets.

There are four species of puffins: Atlantic, Horned, Tufted, and the Rhinoceros Auklet. The last three live in the North Pacific, with southern outposts for Tufted Puffin and Rhinoceros Auklet occurring as far south as the midcoast of California.

Atlantic Puffins nest from Maine east to Greenland, Iceland, Norway, Russia, the British Isles, and along the western coast of France. In North America, they are most numerous in eastern Newfoundland, where about 70% of the continent's puffins live.

We'll be using puffins throughout the guide as a focal species, but we'll be treating them as just one—albeit very popular—member of the greater maritime community.

Gee Whiz Puffin Facts

- Puffins can live for more than 30 years, if they're lucky!
- Puffins can dive to depths of 80 feet or more in search of fish.
- An individual puffin was observed with 61 tiny fish in its bill.
- A puffin can fly about 40 miles an hour, and will beat its wings about 300 to 400 times a minute.
- Puffins usually nest for the first time when they are five years old.
- Puffins lay just one egg a year.
- Puffins usually return to the same burrow and nest with the same mate year after year.

The Four Puffin Species
Atlantic Puffin
Horned Puffin
Rhinoceros Auklet
Tufted Puffin
LUCY GAGLIARDO

- Where soil conditions permit, puffins can tunnel eight feet or more underground when excavating a burrow.
- It is estimated that there are about 6 million pairs of puffins in the world.
- In Iceland puffins are part of a long-standing cultural connection to the sea. They are eaten in restaurants and homes.
- The puffin's number-one natural enemy is the Great Black-backed Gull, which kills and eats adult puffins and chicks when it can catch them.
- Puffins "fly" underwater by flapping their wings for propulsion; they use their webbed feet as rudders.

About Internet Resources

If your school has Internet access, you can use this resource to link with many environmental education programs, news on seabird studies, information on endangered animals, and much, much more. We've listed some web pages below that offer links to all kinds of programs and information. In the bibliographies throughout the book, we've added some Internet resources that are specific to a certain activity. But don't hesitate to do some searching on your own, using one of the many "search engines" available. The Internet is always changing, and you're likely to find new and interesting material with each search.

The Internet is an excellent resource, but student use should always be closely supervised. It's too easy for children to find their way—accidentally or on purpose—to inappropriate material. Always make "surfing" an interactive activity, involving an adult, the students, and the computer, to ensure adequate supervision. Here are some good starting places:

Classroom Resources, Directories, Databases, Catalogs
Includes information on environmental education curricula from various states, catalogs from organizations and video producers, and bibliographies.
http://nceet.snre.umich.edu/classres.html
Environmental Education School Projects, K-12
Links to specific school projects.
http://www.webdirectory.com/Education/K-12/
On-Line Environmental Educator
Links to environmental education centers in Pennsylvania, general environmental education resources, and national organizations.
http://www.state.pa.us/dep.depudate/enved/school-zone.html/
Classroom Resources
Links to various resources such as EarthRise (remote imagery), Classroom Connect, EcoWeb.
http://whale.simmons.edu/environet-stuff/monitoring/resources.html
Aniomal Tracks Program
Classroom resources in air, habitat, people and the environment, wildlife and endangered species, and water, from the National Wildlife Federation.
http:www.nwf.org
Environmental Education Network
Links to programs, projects, and resources.
http://www.envirolink.org.enviroed

Ocean Planet—Smithsonian
A wealth of teacher materials, lesson plans, and fact sheets.
http://seawifs.gsfc.nasa.gov/OCEAN_PLANET/HTML/search_educational_materials.html

Sea World
Includes animal information, quizzes, games, and a grade 4–8 teacher's guide on water.
http://www.bev.net/education/SeaWorld/

VIMS Marine Education
Instructional resources, marine information, "hot topics," etc.
http://www.vims.edu/adv/ed/teach.html

The National Audubon Society
Includes information about Audubon's many programs and publications, including details on Project Puffin and Steve Kress's most recent work with common murres, at Devil's Slide Rock off the coast of California.
http://www.audubon.org/audubon

The Sierra Club
Information about its programs and publications.
http://www.sierraclub.org/

Peterson Home Page
Features a variety of information and publications from the Roger Tory Peterson Institute.
http://www.petersonline.com/

Tweeters
This is a wonderful link to all sorts of information on birds of all types. A lot to explore here!
http://weber.u.washington.edu/dvictor/

Fugleskue Birdwatch
Another page with all sorts of links to bird information all over the world.
http://home.sol.no/tibjonn/

Dennis Lepage Home Page
Yet another linking page, from Canada, with resources around the world and many French-language resources.
http://ntic.qc.ca/~nellas/links.html

The Birder Home Page
Still under construction, with limited information, but worth watching for improvements.
http://www.birder.com

Birdlinks
Numerous links to organizations and programs, pictures of birds, information about birds in specific regions, museums and collections, birds in other countries, etc.
http://www.phys.rug.nl/mk/people/wpv/birdlink.html

Virtual Birder
An online magazine about birds.
http://magneto.cybersmith.com/vbirder/TVBMid.html

Cornell Lab of Ornithology
Information about their resources and programs, including "Citizen Science" volunteer projects (Project FeederWatch, Classroom FeederWatch, Project PigeonWatch), their Library of Natural Sounds, and more.
http://www.ornith.cornell.edu.cs/main.html

Bibliography

Kids Books:

Bailer, Darice. *Puffin's Homecoming*. Smithsonian Wild Heritage Collection, Trudy Management Corp., 1993. Beautiful artwork and a typical story about a puffin's life. For younger students.

Gibbons, Gail. *The Puffins Are Back*. Harper Collins, New York, 1991. Dr. Kress gave technical assistance to this colorful storybook about puffin life, and Project Puffin.

Gove, Doris. *Miracle at Egg Rock*. Down East Books, Camden, Maine, 1985. An anthropomorphic version of Project Puffin, seen from the perspective of one of the transplants. Good for younger students.

Graham, Ada and Frank. *Puffin Island.* Cowles Book Co., 1971. The story of two boys who visit Machias Seal Island to find out how puffins and seabirds live. Photos by Les Line.

Friedman, Judy. *Puffins, Come Back.* Dodd, Meade, New York. 1981. Stephen Kress supplied a number of excellent black and white photographs of the project's early days, as well as guidance in telling the story.

Adult Books:

Atwell, Nancy, editor. *Coming to Know*, Heinemann, 1990. See Chapter 13, "A Puffin is a Bird, I Think," by Jo Haney. This is an intriguing, lively, and useful account by an experienced third grade teacher describing her first attempts at putting together a unit on puffins.

Freethy, Ron. *Auks: An Ornithologist's Guide*. Facts on File, 1987. One of the best all-around studies of the Auk family of birds, with excellent drawings and photos.

Harris, M.P. *The Puffin*. T & A D Poyser, Calton, England 1984. A detailed and authoritative account of puffin biology.

Taylor, Kenny. *Puffins*. Whittet Books Ltd., London 1993.
A popular, less technical account than Harris's—filled with interesting puffin biology.

Internet Resources:

The Puffin Page
A puffin enthusiast's home page, with information about the puffin and some nice photographs.
http://w3.one.net/~lmcbride/rochelle.html

Alcids—Birds of Winter, Stellwagen Bank Information System
http:://vineyard.er.usgs.gov/soundings/alcids.html

Iceland Photographs
Photographs of puffins.
http://www.lonelyplanet.com.au/dest/eur/graphics/ice15.htm

Theme I: Puffins and Seabirds are Magnificently Adapted to Living on the Ocean

Most passengers on board our summertime puffin-watching boat trips are amazed to learn that puffins spend their entire fall, winter, and early spring at sea. People shake their heads in disbelief when they learn that puffins actually survive the cold, the wind, and the great storms of the North Atlantic. We try to impress upon them that puffins are seabirds, and that they've evolved over time to thrive in that seemingly harsh and unlivable environment. Humans tend to project their own thoughts and feelings onto animals, and the idea of living on and in a cold, "trackless" ocean is hard to even imagine.

What are some of the ways that puffins and other seabirds survive? The following activities look at the properties of a feather, camouflage, the design of various beaks, how puffins swim while underwater, etc.

Activity 1: Look, Ma, It's a Combination Raincoat and Winter Jacket

Objective: To understand what a feather is, what's down, and how they function.

Time: One period.

Materials: Large wing feathers (from a farm or store)
Down
Magnifying glasses
Low-power microscopes.

Methods: Begin by passing a large wing feather in a circle. Each student suggests one word to describe how it looks to him or her, but cannot repeat what has already been said. If the group is small, or the words seem to come too easily, pass it around again as an added challenge. Do the same with a sample of down.

Move the activity into a discussion about possible functions of the feather and down.

Split up into small groups and have the children look at larger feathers under a magnifying glass. Ask them to

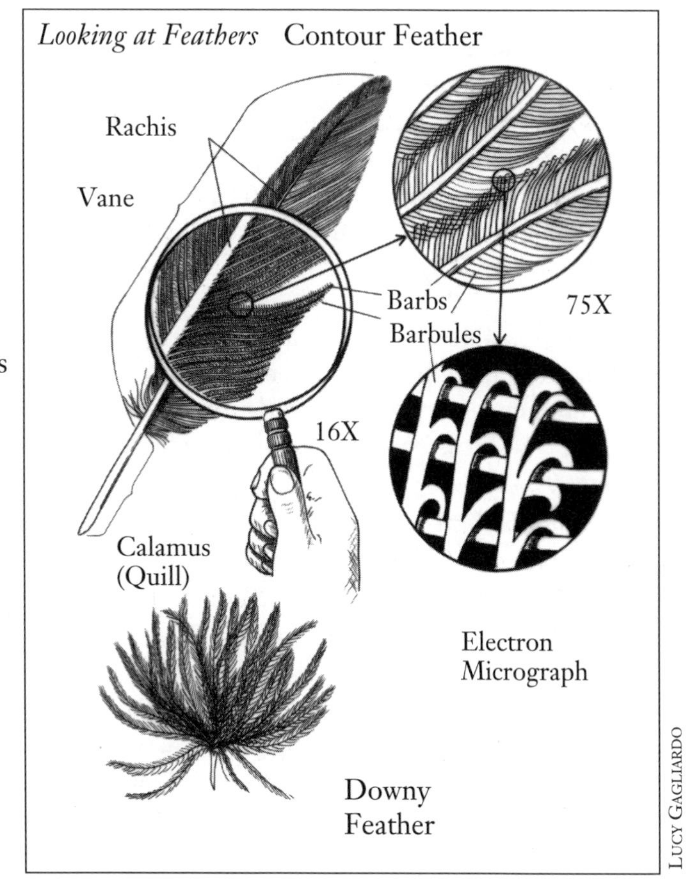

draw what they see. Do the same with a feather under a low-power microscope. They can spread portions of the feather apart with a pencil point or their fingers.

Students won't see the extensive interlocking web of tiny hooks and barbs that keep the feather flattish, stiff, and water repellent because it takes an electron microscope to show that. But ask students to draw a detail of their feather that shows any visible aspect of this weblike structure. Do the same with the down. They'll be quite aware of its springiness. (Down is the most effective insulator known because of its ability to trap air, which then warms near the bird's body.)

Activity 2: Oil's Deadly Deeds

Objectives: To observe the effect that water, different oils, and detergent have on bird's feathers.

Time: One period.

Materials: Large and small feathers
Cooking oil
New or used motor oil
"Dawn" dishwashing detergent
Paper towels
Eyedroppers
Small bowls of water.

Methods: Have students work in pairs. Float a feather in the bowl of water and take one drop of water at a time and drop it on the feather. Observe what happens. Then put a drop or two of cooking oil on the feather. Let it "soak" in. Try again with drops of water and see what happens. Does the water roll off?

Use motor oil on a clean feather as you did with the cooking oil. Then drop water onto it. What happens? Then see what happens when students try to clean the feather with a drop or two of detergent. Tell them to keep rinsing until clean water begins to bead up on the feather. This may take more time than they might have imagined. But it's a good, though greatly simplified, way of showing them how "oiled" birds are cleaned in field conditions, and how arduous a task it really is.

As a supplement to this activity, see what it takes to "clean up" the "oil spill" you've created by trying out the following materials: cotton balls, cardboard, styrofoam, spoons, paper towels, aquarium nets. Attempt to get the motor oil out of the water. Record your results on a chart, showing the efficacy of each method tried. Add some detergent to the oil spill and see what happens.

Discussion: Oil destroys a feather's waterproofing qualities because it breaks down the "zip-locking" structure. Birds may die of hypothermia because the cold sea water can reach their skin, or because of the toxic effects of ingested oil as they attempt to preen or clean their feathers. (Stomach ulcers may develop from oil ingestion. Oil can also damage eggs and nestlings.)

This is a good lead-in to showing photos of oil spills like that of the EXXON VALDEZ, and studying what happened to marine life. What do students think can be done? Some important steps *have* been taken, such as legislation to compel tanker owners to build double-hulled vessels. What about the larger issue of our reliance on fossil fuels? This may be an appropriate place to talk about non-renewable vs. renewable energies. Once students understand the impact of oil on seabirds, they can start considering how to cut down on their own uses.

Activity 3: Beaks

Introduction: While humans have created a great variety of tools, birds use various body parts as tools. Examples are feet, toenails, talons, and beaks. The variety of bird beaks is incredible. The Leach's Storm-petrel has a tiny, thin bill that it uses to pluck small organisms off the ocean's surface. In contrast, the puffin has a broad, compressed bill designed to catch and hold many slippery fish.

Objective: To learn that each type of beak is designed for specific kinds of food items.

Time: One to two periods.

Setting-Up and Overview: There are a number of different items you'll need for this activity, but it's well worth the effort.

There will be four stations around the room. Each station will feature a specific "food," and several tools (beaks), which may or may not be well designed for collecting that food item. Groups of three to six students will go from one station to the other, trying different tools. (If you decide to let *each* student try *each* of the three different tools at every station, it will take much longer to do the activity.) They will be doing this within a timed period. Experiment with the actual time—start with two minutes and see how that works. They will also be recording their data during the post-capture period. After they complete the circuit, lead a discussion about their observations and discoveries, i.e., which tools worked best, worst, etc. Then loosely compare tools with pictures of real bird beaks. For example, a puffin's beak compares to serrated pliers, or pliers, or even chopsticks.

Materials: Stopwatch

The "beaks" or tools are as follows:

- About 8 pairs of chopsticks
- 4 teaspoons
- 4 pairs of serrated pliers
- 2 pair of tweezers
- A dozen toothpicks
- 2 small strainers
- 2 pair of regular pliers

The "food" list is as follows:

- A dozen or more small (the size of a flattened pea) pieces of soap
- A dozen walnuts
- A hunk of clay the size of a softball

A cupful of dried cracked pieces of popcorn or puffed rice
Two bowls of water
A pound of dry macaroni shells
A handful of red pistachio nuts or dried kidney beans

Station 1 Food: Small pieces of soap in a large bowl or aquarium. This is analogous to slippery fish. (If you have an air bubbler in an aquarium, it will move the water around, and make the experiment more realistic.) Tools: Chopsticks, a teaspoon, serrated pliers. Birds that eat these small fish: puffins, terns, guillemots, murres, razorbills.

Station 2 Food: Walnuts stuck in a matrix of clay. this is analogous to mussels stuck onto rocks. Tools: A spoon, chopsticks, serrated pliers. Birds that pull mussels off underwater substrate: eider ducks.

Station 3 Food: Cracked pieces of popcorn or puffed rice floating in a large bowl or an aquarium, similar to Station 1. Use old popcorn because it is more brittle and will easily crack. (Once again, an air bubbler or filter will move the water around and increase the effect.) This is analogous to macroplankton such as crustaceans and animal larvae floating on the surface of the ocean, which storm-petrels eat. Tools: Tweezers, chopsticks, sharp toothpicks.

Station 4 Food: Dry, hard macaroni shells in a bowl. Color a few dozen with nail polish, or use red pistachio nuts or kidney beans spread amongst the macaroni. The macaroni is gravel, rocks, and debris on a beach or island shore; the colored items are washed up bits of food like dead crabs, fish, urchins, garbage. Birds that eat this: gulls. Tools: Small strainer, chopsticks, pliers.

Methods: Each member of a group tries one tool at each station. Tell kids they *can't use fingers or anything else* to make the job easier. Have them create this chart in their notebook:

Chart for Beaks	"Beak"	How many food items did all your group members capture in time period?	Total number of captured items for entire class.
Station 1 (Fish)	Spoon		
	Chopsticks		
	Serrated Pliers		
Station 2 (Mussels)	Spoon		
	Chopsticks		
	Serrated Pliers		
Station 3 (Macroplankton)	Tweezers		
	Chopsticks		
	Toothpicks		
Station 4 (Beach Debris)	Strainer		
	Chopsticks		
	Pliers		

After each stop, students can record what happened. If you're recording how well each student did using every tool, you can ask the students to figure out the averages.

Put the same chart on the blackboard and have each group add its numbers to each category. Open discussion to a sharing of experiences.

Look at actual pictures/photos of birds showing their beaks (see illustration). Based on shapes of beaks alone, discuss feeding patterns of different seabirds. (See illustration of seabird feeding strategies.) Discuss feeding behaviors that birds must have in order to use their beaks. Look at pictures of common landbirds (woodpecker, finch, nuthatch) and ask what they might be adapted to eat.

Activity 4: Why Puffins Don't Freeze

Objective: To feel how a layer of fat helps insulate the body from the chilling effects of cold water.

Time: Half a period, or so.

Materials: A can or two of Crisco shortening
A dozen or more quart-sized, zipping plastic bags
Duct tape
Several basins of icy, cold water

Method: Measure one cup of shortening and place it in a quart-sized zipping plastic bag. Turn a second bag inside out and put it inside the bag with the shortening, being sure to reverse the zipper tracks. Zip the bags together. For added protection, seal the bags around the zipper with duct tape. Push the shortening around, from the outside, to distribute it evenly in the "mitt."

For each mitt with shortening, make an empty mitt, without shortening. These mitts will be used to compare with the insulated models.

Give each student a chance to place one hand in an empty mitt and one in an insulated mitt (with the shortening). Then ask the student place both hands in a basin or sink of icy, cold water. What happens? (Since this process doesn't take very long, you can get by with making only a few sets of mitts and taking turns with them.)

Discussion: While it is well known that marine mammals such as whales, seals, and polar bears have thick layers of fat to help keep them warm, northern seabirds such as puffins also rely on internal layers of fat to help them survive frigid arctic waters. This fat, combined with their external water-repelling and air-trapping coat of feathers, allows seabirds to live in a seemingly harsh environment. (Older students could research other adaptations to the cold, for birds as well as other life forms.)

Activity 5: Puffins Win Olympic Swim Meet!

Objective: To see how well puffins are adapted to swimming underwater.

Setting: A public aquarium with a seabird exhibit. (See end of book for a list)

Method: Watch puffins or auks or penguins swim. Some specific questions you can ask students include:

How long do puffins stay underwater?
Do puffins seem to change color underwater? If so, why might this be?
How do puffins use their wings under water?

How do they use their feet underwater? How do they use them at the surface?

Do they dive with their eyes open?

Also, you might want students to record a timed behavior sequence, such as what an individual bird does during a certain time period. One suggested way to do this is to list all the behaviors they see, giving each a name. In what order do the birds perform these behaviors? Rank the behaviors from most common to least common. Do all puffins act the same? As a comparison, contrast two or three individuals.

Discussion: It can be a very enlightening experience for children to see how fast, efficient, and streamlined the birds are underwater. It's a startling juxtaposition to seeing a bird fly, walk, or sit on the water. Adult puffins not only have to catch enough fish for themselves to eat, but also enough to feed a hungry chick (about 100 grams a day). They also have to be able to swim faster than the fish do! This activity also gives students a somewhat realistic picture of how birds spend their time.

Activity 6: Now You See It, Now You Don't

Objective: To understand why puffins and many other seabirds are colored (black and white) the way they are. This activity is all about camouflage.

Time: One period to get models painted and one to do the experiment.

Key Point: Puffins are vulnerable to avian predators such as gulls and jaegers, and they are vulnerable to underwater predators such as bluefish and sharks.

Materials: Choose whatever materials for the simulated body of the puffin that are most accessible to you: Closed plastic quart jugs, styrofoam meat packing trays, or large styrofoam balls, i.e., 4–6 inches in diameter.
Five or six different colors of acrylic paint
Paintbrushes
A portable kiddie pool or something similar
Two or three aquariums with glass bottoms

Methods: Paint one half of a jug or tray with white paint and the other side with black. Do this for five or six other jugs, and use different color combinations. If you have a lot of jugs or trays, you can have each student paint individual color combinations. Let them experiment with stripes, dots, etc. Let the paint dry.

For aerial views, float jugs in pool, but prepare the pool so the bottom is dark rather than light. This would be analogous to looking down at the surface of the ocean, which is dark. Perhaps you might have to place a cut-open gray or black plastic bag on the pool bottom. Once the camouflage models are floating in water, obtain an aerial vantage point. If you are doing this outside, you could look down from a second story window; if you are indoors, use a ladder. Ask students to rank which colors blend in the best. You can make a chart on the board or have students make individual charts in their notebooks for this and the following part of this activity.

Conduct a similar observation of the bird bellies, this time using the clear-bottomed aquariums. Position the aquariums between two tabletops, for example, so that a student can lie down on the rug under the aquarium and see the floating bird above him or her. Ideally, this should be done outside so that the sky is the medium you're looking up into, but you can do it in a classroom with a light ceiling. Which colors blend in the best, and which don't? Does this fit with the naturally occurring colors of the puffin's body?

Typical charts for "Now You See It, Now You Don't":

Color of "puffin" on top	*Did it blend in well?*
White	(no)
Black	(yes)
Red	(?)
Green, etc.	(?)

Looking up at bird's belly	*Did it blend in well?*
White	(yes)
Black	(no)
Red	(?)
Green, etc.	(?)

Activity 7: Let's Molt!

Objective: To compare the changes in an adult puffin's appearance between summer and winter plumage, and fledgling (six-week-old) plumage.

Time: One period.

Materials: Use the provided worksheets
Colored pencils or thin-point markers for coloring

Methods: Have the children color in the various parts of a fledgling puffin, and an adult in both summer and winter plumage, according to the color scheme provided.

Discussion: Talk over the advantages of color for courtship purposes, and for camouflage in the ocean environment. For example, why do puffins have such big, colorful beaks? (Let students come up with their own answers first.) Ideas from scientists include: 1) Bright colors help to attract a mate. 2) The possibility that bigger beaks may be a badge of experience, corresponding to age. Puffin beaks get larger with age, up to a point, and those puffins with very large beaks may make the best mates since they have proven their ability to survive over time.

1. Yellow
2. Red-Orange
3. Orange
4. Blue-Gray
5. Black
6. Light Gray
7. Dark Gray
8. Dull Yellow
9. Red-Orange Brown
10. White

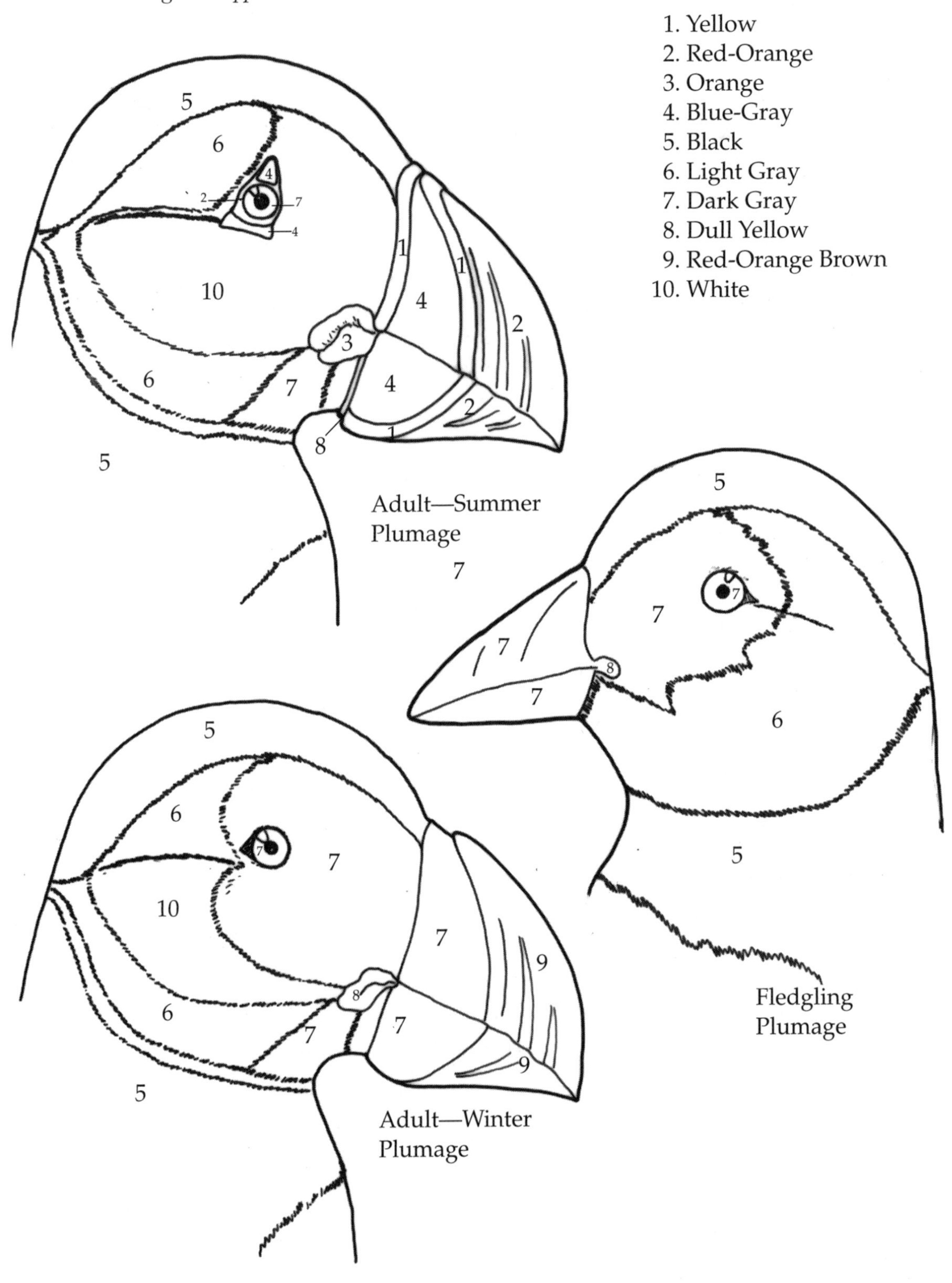

LUCY GAGLIARDO

3) Big beaks help support hefty loads of fish while the birds fly long distances from feeding areas to nesting islands.

Look over field guide plates or color photos of *other* birds for comparison. You might ask the question: Why do males and females of the same species have different plumages? For example, a male cardinal is more colorful than its female counterpart, yet male and female puffins are identical. In species where the sexes are identical, both male and female share *all* duties at the nest. In contrast, cardinals, most warblers, and other sexually dimorphic (different) birds have separate and individual duties. For instance, in many species the female does the incubating. Perhaps then, one reason for these plumage differences is to keep track of the division of labor. (These are complex issues in ornithology and have been studied for years; there are oftentimes no easy answers!)

Activity 8: Where do Atlantic Puffins Live?

Objective: Children learn the whereabouts of the world's major Atlantic Puffin colonies, as well as how many breeding pairs are estimated to be in each area.

Materials: Several world atlases and world maps suitable for tracing, tracing paper

Time: One period or more, depending on how much math and graphing you do.

Background Information: Approximately 5,880,000 pairs of Atlantic Puffins exist in the world. They nest from 44 degrees north to 79 degrees north, from Eastern Egg Rock, Maine, to islands north of Russia in the arctic. These breeding populations are not distributed at random, but are found primarily in biologically rich areas where different water masses meet, such as the intersection of cold arctic waters and warmer Atlantic waters. This mixing helps bring about high productivity of plankton, crustaceans, fish, etc. (See Theme II, Activity 5.)

The following information sums up where puffins occur in the world:

- Gulf of Maine: Eastern Egg Rock, Matinicus Rock, Seal Island, Petit Manan Island, Machias Seal Island (Canada). Approximately 1,200–1,500 pairs.
- Newfoundland: Witless Bay (in Eastern Newfoundland); Great Island, Green Island, Gull Island, etc. 270,000 pairs, 6% of world's total.
- Labrador: Approximately 87,000 pairs on 17 islands.
- Greenland: About 31 colonies, near Thule, Kitsigsorssuit, on the western side of the island. About 4,000 pairs.
- Iceland: Many colonies around the entire country, with about 3,000,000 breeding pairs, or 51% of the world's total.
- Faeroe Islands: 500,000 pairs, or 8% of world's total.
- British Isles: A total of 720,000 pairs in Scotland, Ireland, and England, or about 12% of the world's population, as follows: Scotland—Outer and Inner Hebrides, Shetland Islands, Orkney Islands, etc., 645,000 pairs. England—Farne Islands, Channel Islands, etc., 20,000 pairs. Wales—Skomer Island, etc., 10,000 pairs. Ireland—45,000 pairs on west coast.
- France: Less than 200 pairs off Brittany, in northwest France.
- Norway: A total of 1,258,000 pairs in 29 locations, or 21% of the world's total population. Found in Lofoten Islands, Nordland, Troms, Rost, etc.
- Spitsbergen (an island owned by Norway): About 10,000 pairs in 18 colonies.
- Kola Peninsula on the Murmansk Coast of Russia: About 16,300 pairs in 11 colonies.
- Novaya Zemlya (northern Russia): About 300 pairs in 5 locations on the west coast.

Suggested Graphic Aids for "Where Do Puffins Live":

1. Bar graph showing distribution

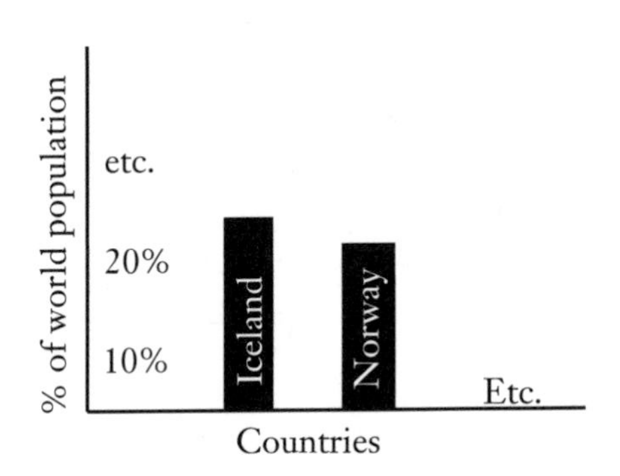

2. Pie graph showing distribution

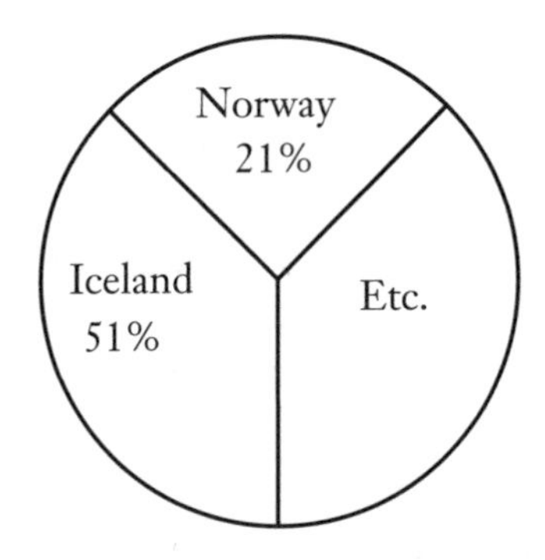

Methods: Have your students trace the Northern Hempsphere from a world map and give a copy of the above data for each student or each team. Have them find the locations by looking at either an overhead projection of the North Atlantic or by using atlases in the library, and then have them label each important country and island. Then they can fill in the estimated numbers at each location.

For mathematical problems, ask them to figure out what percentages of the world's puffin population each area holds. Bar graphs and pie charts are good ways to show different percentages.

Activity 9: Find Your Seabird Partners by Voice.

Objective: By listening to several different seabird voices on the seabird tape, students learn how birds such as puffins, gulls, and terns sound. Then a brief but fun game with individual students giving the calls of specific birds brings the activity to closure.

Time: Half to full period.

Materials: *Voices of Maine Seabirds* audiocassette, available for $10 postpaid from National Audubon, 159 Sapsucker Woods Rd., Ithaca, NY 14850.

Cassette player

A large open space, perhaps the size of a classroom or half of a gymnasium

Background Information: Animals have different ways of communicating with each other. Seabirds use their voices, as well as a variety of body-language postures. Some vocalizations are meant as cries of aggression, of warning, or for communicating location.

Methods: Listen to the sounds of puffins, gulls, etc. Play several of the most interesting or the most easily duplicable to your students. Ask students to try their impressions of each one. After you've gone through perhaps six or seven, assign (in secret) two or three students to each seabird voice. Don't let anyone know anyone else's assignment, and tell the children not to give away their identities. Spread the students around a large open room, or outdoors, and at the sound of the word "Go," tell each student to give his or her call a number of times. Kids walk around calling in an attempt to find others who are giving the same call. When they do, they stay together.

When most or all students find their partners, tell them to freeze. Then go from one group to another asking each one to give their call. Ask the other students to guess that group's identity.

Activity 10: A Ten-Minute Flapping Puffin

Objective: Turn an envelope into a simple but fun finger puppet.

Time: Ten minutes, or so.

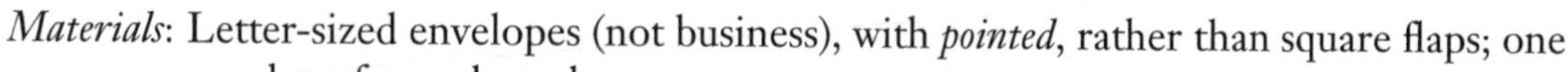

Materials: Letter-sized envelopes (not business), with *pointed*, rather than square flaps; one envelope for each student
- Transparent tape
- Scissors
- Crayons or markers
- Aluminum foil, feathers, sequins, glue (all optional)

1. Carefully unstick the glued flaps of an envelope and spread it out in front of you, inside facing up.

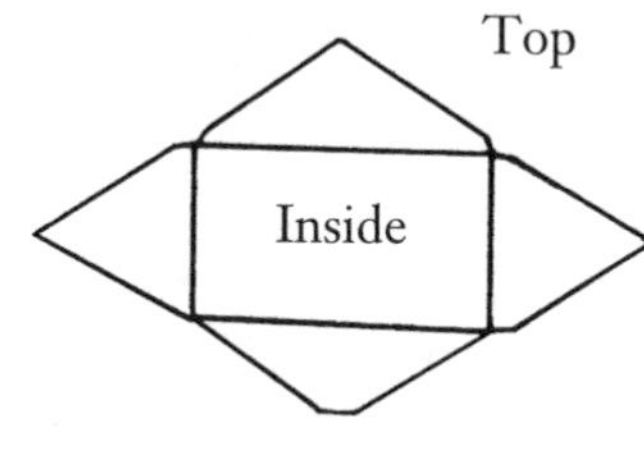

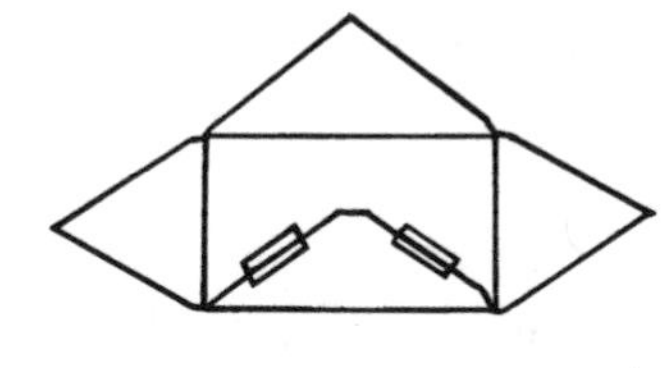

2. Fold the bottom flap of the envelope back in place and secure it with two pieces of tape along the sides.

3. Fold the envelope in half from right to left, so that the side flaps meet. You can lick the glue on the top flap to seal the two halves of it together.

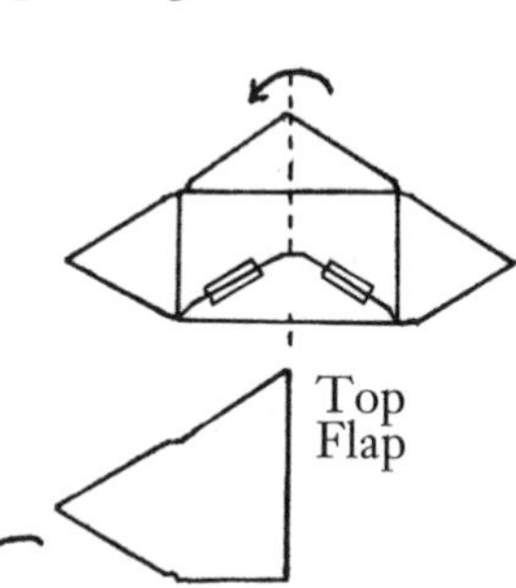

4. Now turn the envelope 90° so that the side flaps point down. These will be the wings.

5. Look at a photograph of a puffin and see the beautiful colors of its beak and face. Draw the puffin's head and wings on your puppet. On one side of the face, draw fish in the puffin's beak. If you have feathers, you can glue them on the puffin's wings, and aluminum foil or sequins can be added to the fish.

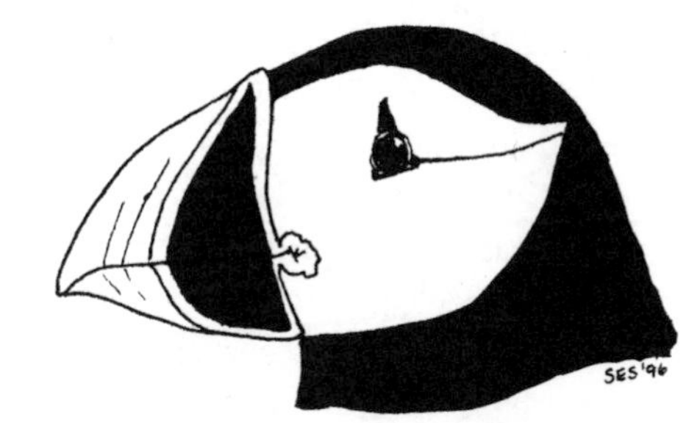

6. Carefully cut a sliver off both halves of the puppet so that you can slide your middle and index fingers into the slots that are formed. Move your fingers to make the puppet flap its wings!

7. The puffin flies away to sea—and then it returns to its chick with a beak full of fish!

Activity 11: Making Puffin Decoys

Objective: Students make puffin decoys by sculpting clay or salt dough, or by using papier mâché. You can introduce this activity by saying that these models will be similar to Project Puffin's early use of decoys on Eastern Egg Rock. (The sculpted ones will actually be about half-size.) During puffin and tern restoration in Maine, decoys were used to lure birds to the islands. (See discussion of this in *Project Puffin*.) Decoys are currently used in the Seabird Restoration Program to lure murres, Laysan Albatrosses, and Northern Gannets to safe breeding sites.

Materials: With a kiln: White clay. This material is gray before it's fired, but comes out a fine white color.

Without a kiln:

Salt dough: The recipe for three or four children is 4 cups flour, 1 cup salt, 1½ cups of water. Mix and knead to the consistency of stiff bread dough. You can use a food processor. This material can be worked by your students for a half day or so before it begins to dry out. If you want to make it beforehand, you can keep it in the refrigerator for a few days in a plastic bag, but let it warm up to room temperature before working it. Salt dough decoys will air-dry on newspaper but must be turned every day or so. You can also use a 200° oven, if you prefer.

Papier-mâché: Try making full-sized puffin models from papier-mâché. "Pritt" Art Paste is a new and excellent material; it's a powder that is mixed with water. Follow directions on the box for mixing. Strips of newspaper can easily be torn several layers at a time into 1- to 1½-inch-wide strips. Saturate strips in glue mixture (the Pritt paste, flour and water mixed to a light cream consistency, or wallpaper paste mixed to package directions). Apply the strips over wadded-up newspaper that's taped together. This serves as your foundation. Paint with acrylics or tempera, and use a fixative (see below) on tempera.

Tempera or acrylic paints
Paintbrushes
Liqui-tex acrylic gloss medium
Small ⅛-inch or ¼-inch dowels

Methods for Sculpting: Students will be shaping their clay or salt dough into a half-size replica of a puffin, about five to six inches tall. (A full-size model would use a lot of clay!) To make a stand for each "decoy," push a short piece of a wooden dowel an inch or so into the base of the clay while it is still wet, but then remove it. If you're using salt dough, you can push the dowel in and leave it there while the piece dries. Use a rounded mound of clay or salt dough with a dowel hole in it as the base, and make this at the same time that you're making the puffin.

Once the pieces are dry, paint them. Then put on a *light* coat of the Liqui-tex acrylic gloss medium, which is a fixative for tempera. You could use a clear shellac or a spray fixative instead. Acrylic paint, however, does not need this fixative. But it does need a few hours or overnight to dry, while tempera dries in an hour or so.

Activity 12: Puffin Puppets

A Puffin Puppet

LUCY GAGLIARDO

Objective: Each student can make his or her own puppet from felt and clay.

Materials: Black felt for the body
White felt for the belly
Orange felt for the legs and feet
Use clay or salt dough for the head
A hot glue gun or Elmer's glue for gluing the head into place
Staplers or sewing materials

Methods: Use copies of the template for proper sizing and shape (copy patterns at 130%). Have students hold the templates on the

A Pattern for the Puppet (enlarge pattern to 130%)

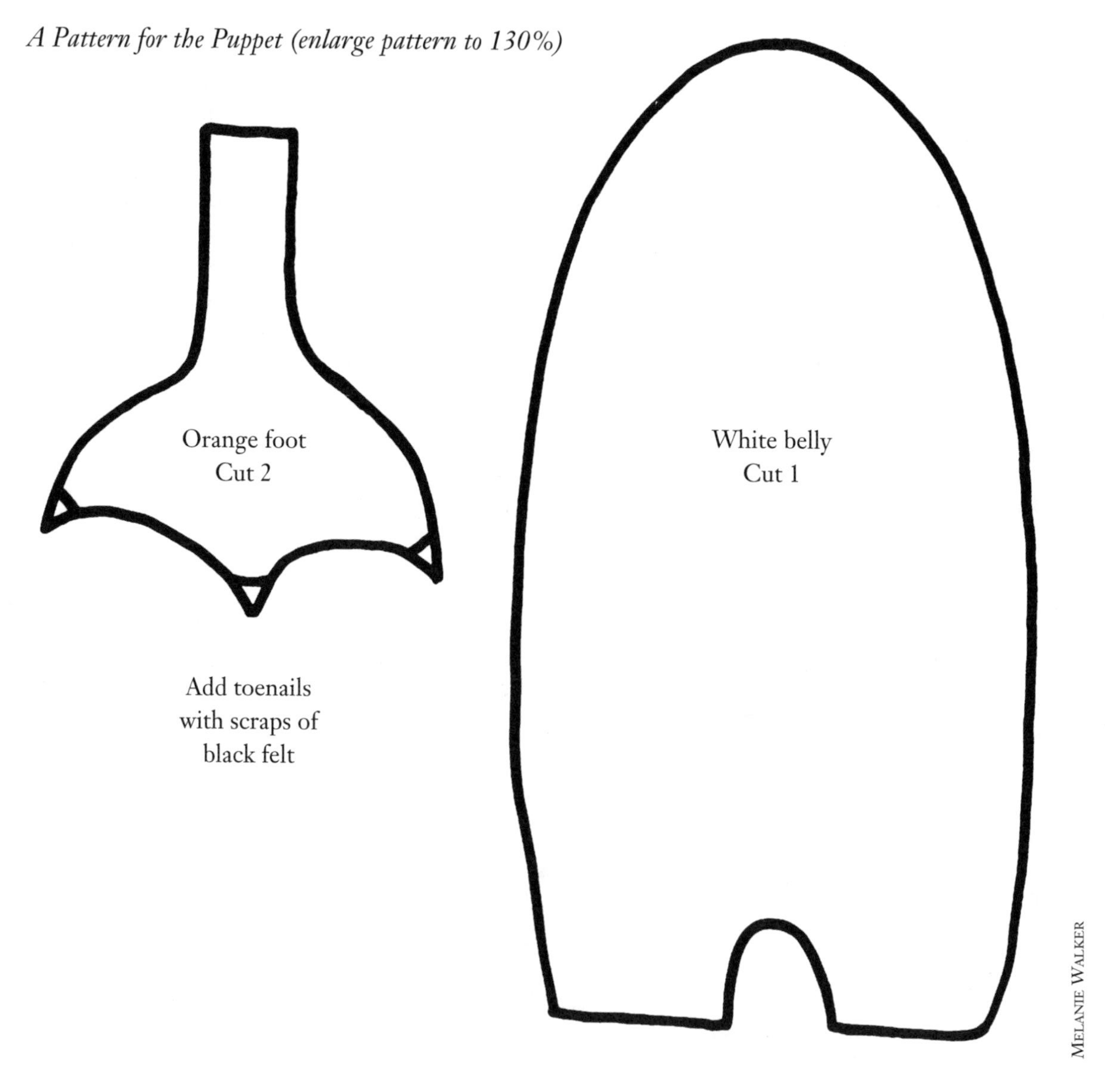

MELANIE WALKER

A Pattern for the Puppet (enlarge pattern to 130%)

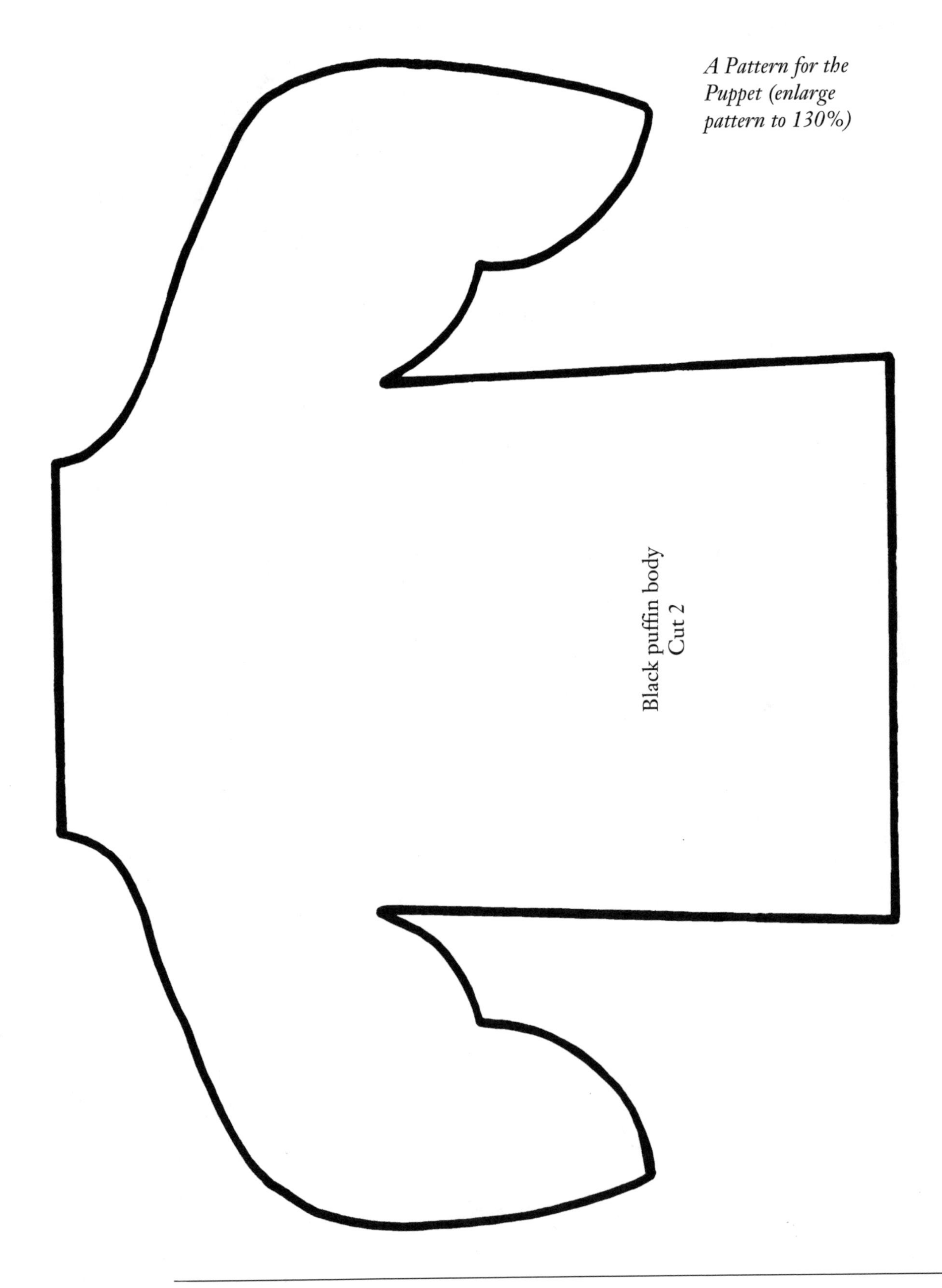

felt pieces and trace with white chalk or a marker. Then, cut them out. Be sure to cut two—one for the front and one for the back. Sew or glue on belly and feet to the front piece. Felt body pieces can then be sewn or stapled together to make a full-sized puffin look-a-like. The head can be made beforehand by sticking two fingers into the ball of clay (which will need to be kiln-fired later) or salt dough, and then by sculpting features like the beak and the neck while the head is still on your fingers. When you have finished sculpting, carefully remove your fingers from the clay or salt dough and set the head aside to dry. (Air-dry, then kiln-fire if using clay; for salt dough, air-dry for about a week, turning every day, or oven-dry in a 200° oven until hard, about two to three hours.)

Use a hot glue gun or Elmer's glue to attach the head to the felt body, one side at a time. Sew the white belly and orange legs into their appropriate places. Use black felt tips for toenails.

Consider creating a stage and other puppet seabirds such as gulls, terns, cormorants, etc.

Activity 13: A Puffin Model from Paper

Objective: Students color and assemble puffin models. (You can make mobiles from these models by fastening a string to the appropriate place.)

Time: One to two periods.

Materials: Photocopies of original template on heavy paper for each student
Crayons, paints, colored pencils, or felt-tip markers
Scissors
Glue
String (optional).

Methods: Follow directions on the templates on pages 22 and 23.

Activity 14: A Seabird Mural

Objective: Have a group of children or your class make a large mural of a typical seabird nesting island.

Materials: Standard-sized mural paper, which is 36 inches wide
Tempera paint
Brown construction paper for three-dimensional rocks.

Methods: Decide what your basic scene will look like; i.e., an ocean habitat with an island, sky, birds, seals, etc. Sketch out these habitat scenes first (the landform, surrounding ocean and sky), then have students paint them in. Crumpled pieces of brown construction paper can be glued and mounted for a three-dimensional effect. For the animals, have each child work at his or her own desk or table with sheets of 9x12-inch or 12x18-inch construction or white paper. They can draw, color, paint, cut it out, and then mount their creations on the larger mural. Puffins, gulls, cormorants, ducks, terns, and seals are popular animals. Fish and whales can be placed underwater, as can birds swimming in pursuit of fish.

Activity 15: Seabird Quilt or Wallhanging of Felt

Objective: This project is similar to the previous one, but uses pieces of felt.

Materials: A large piece of light blue felt as the background, about 6x3 feet.

Activity 13
A Pattern for the Puffin Model (enlarge pattern to 130%)

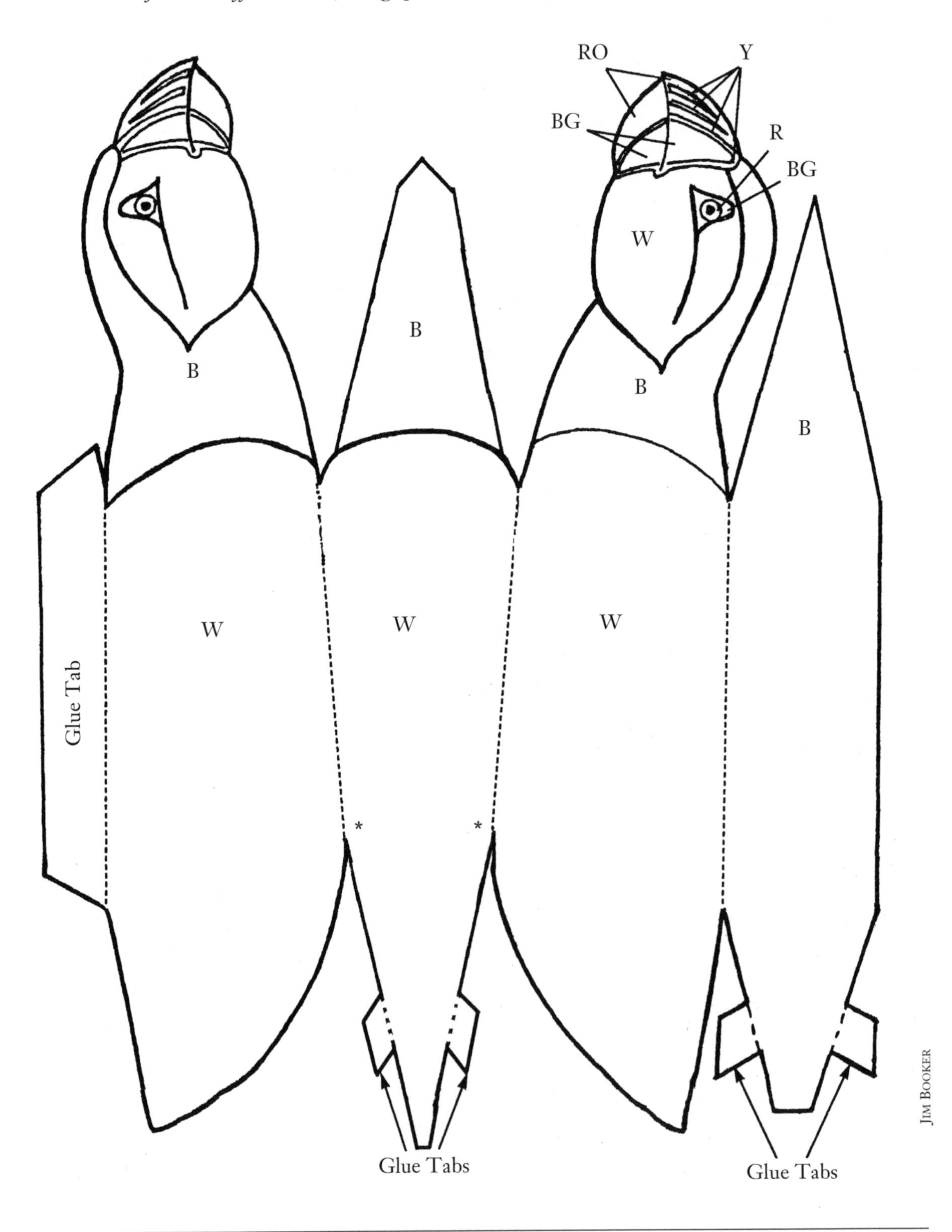

Activity 13
A Pattern for the Puffin Model
(enlarge pattern to 130%)

1. Photocopy originals and cut out the pattern (heavy paper suggested).
2. Color the pieces using the color code key.
3. Carefully fold the body along the dotted lines.
4. Glue the body into a tube shape, using the large glue tab.
5. Glue the nape piece to the breast triangle piece.
6. Glue the two sides of the bill together, keeping the pieces even.
7. Glue the tabs to their appropriate places.
8. Glue the wing section to the back.
9. Glue the two feet at the points marked with a *.

O—Orange
B—Black
W—White
R—Red
Y—Yellow
BG—Blue Gray
RO—Red Orange

Different colored felt pieces
Scissors
Glue

Method: Glue gray felt and dark blue or blue-green felt on the light blue background to make a seabird nesting island. Students make felt cut-outs to place on the scene.

Seabird Quilt or Wallhanging of Felt:

Light blue background
Brown felt
Dark blue felt
Grey felt

LUCY GAGLIARDO

Activity 16: Seabird Quilt or Wallhanging, Using Fabric Transfer Crayons

Objective: Each student can contribute a "square" to this project, as desired.

Materials: Fabric transfer crayons (can be purchased at craft or art stores. The crayons are used on paper and then the paper with the design on it is ironed onto fabric and the design transfers.)

Fabric—a white bedsheet is recommended.
Pencils
White paper cut into 6x6-inch squares (photocopy paper or newsprint is fine.)

Method: Students first sketch their drawing with pencil onto their 6-inch-square of paper. Stress large, bold pictures—remember, they will have to be colored in with crayon, which has a much wider tip than pencil. Next, students color their drawing with fabric transfer crayons. Drawings look especially nice when bright colors are used and shapes are outlined with black crayon. Do not write any words or names on your design—they will transfer backwards! If names or words are desired, add them on directly to fabric *after* you have transferred the design.

Lay out squares on the bedsheet leaving about two inches in between each square. Cut bedsheet to appropriate size. Turn over each paper design and put a clean piece of paper over it. An adult should iron—and thereby transfer—each square in the appropriate place. (See directions on back of crayon box.) Bind edges and hang as is, or sew on a colorful border, add quilt batting and a back sheet, bind edges and tie at each corner of each square with yarn.

A Seabird Quilt or Wallhanging:

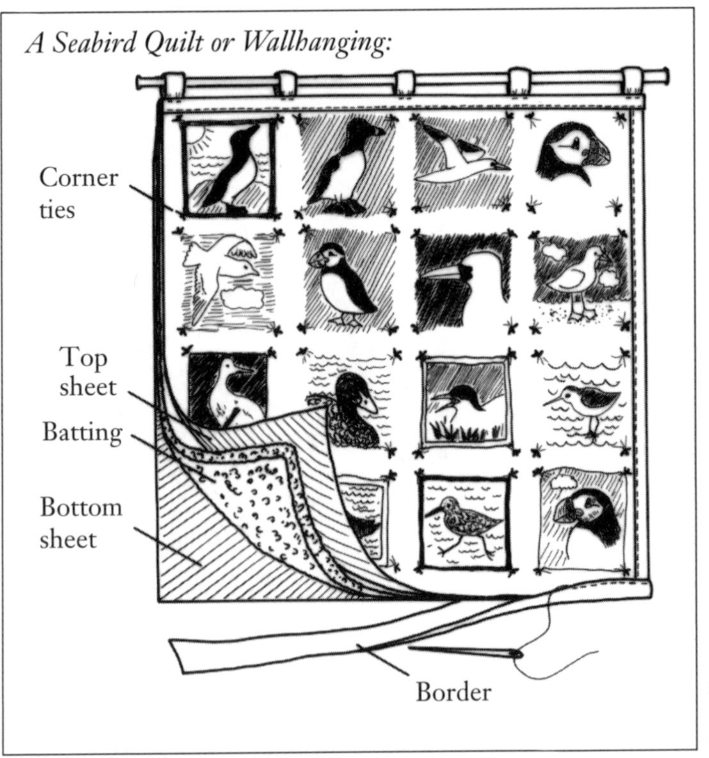

LUCY GAGLIARDO

Bibliography

Kids Books:

Berger, Melvin. *Oil Spill.* Harper Collins, 1994. For younger readers; big colorful paintings, accessible text.

Bremner, Tony. *How Birds Live.* Usborne, 1978.

Burnie, David. *Bird.* Eyewitness

Books, Knopf, 1988. Great photos and eye-catching layout; text seems more appropriate to middle school students.
Daly, Kathleen. *The Big Golden Book of Backyard Birds.* Golden Books, 1990. Beautiful large paintings of common birds and a paragraph of text on each.
Kress, Steve. *Bird Life.* Golden Press, 1991. A concise and complete guide to bird biology. Many illustrations.
Markle, Sandra. *Outside and Inside Birds.* Bradbury Press, New York, 1994. How birds live, with photos of internal anatomy, etc.
McMillan, Bruce. *A Beach For The Birds.* Houghton Mifflin, New York, 1993. A nicely illustrated life history of endangered Least Terns.
Patent, Dorothy. *Feathers.* Cobblehill Books, Dutton, New York, 1992. Describes in text and photographs birds' feathers—from structure, type, and color to various uses.
Ranger Rick's NatureScope, *Birds, Birds, Birds.* National Wildlife Federation, 1989. An excellent activity guide (K-6). Can also be used for activities in Theme VI.
Wharton, Anthony. *Discovering Seabirds.* Bookwright Press, New York, 1987. An excellent, generously illustrated introduction to the subject. Delves into various aspects of seabirds' lives.
Riccuiti, Edward. *Birds.* Blackbirch Press, Connecticut. 1993. Part of the "Our Living World" series. Examines the physical structure, metabolism, and lifestyle of birds, and discusses how they fit into the food chain.
Wildlife Education Ltd., (San Diego ZooBooks), *Seabirds.* April 1995 issue, Wildlife Education, Ltd. A beautifully illustrated eighteen-page booklet on the lives of seabirds. Excellent.
Van Cleave, Janis. *Janis van Cleave's Microscopes and Magnifying Lenses.* John Wiley 1993. Offers specific activities.

Adult Books: (Also see bibliography after this book's Introduction)

Fisher, J. and Lockley, R.M. *Seabirds.* Bloomsbury Books (London) 1989. A classic and comprehensive survey of North Atlantic seabirds by two renowned experts.

Internet Resources:

Ocean News Issue #3: Seabirds, "The Two Lives of Diving Seabirds," "Seabirds, Oil, and You," "Oil and Feathers Don't Mix," and "Build an Alcid: A Biological Design Challenge."
http://oceanlink.idland.net/seabirds.html

Oil Pollution
Sources, accidents, cleanups.
http://seawifs/gsfc.nasa.gov:80/OCEAN_PLANET/HTML/peril_oil_pollution.html

Virtual Marine Education Center
Includes information on doing a marine project or report, and marine education topics links
http://www.vims.edu/adv/ed/stu.html

Also, see some of the general bird resources on the Internet, listed on pages 4–5.

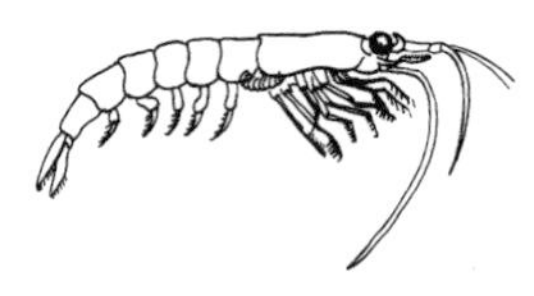

Theme II: A Healthy Marine Ecosystem is the "Invisible" Support for Seabird Colonies, and Other Ocean Inhabitants

Introduction

From atop the lighthouse tower on Matinicus Rock on a July day, you can look down and see more than a hundred sausage-shaped Harbor Seals hauled out on the rocks for their daily snooze, as well as dozens of cormorants, gulls, and eider ducks sitting on the water or resting up on the granite boulders. Off to another side, there are a thousand or more screaming terns flying in and out of their nesting colony, many with fish in their bills. On a nearby cliff, sixty or seventy puffins and razorbills are congregating. It's a dazzling sight, all that life! And beyond the island's perimeter, the sparkling gray-green waters of Penobscot Bay stretch into the distance.

These fertile coastal waters that surround seabird islands like Matinicus Rock are rich with untold trillions of microscopic plants and animals (plankton) that form the foundation of the so-called food web. The excitement of seeing seals and seabirds, and the occasional whale or porpoise is possible *only* because of the successful functioning of the entire regional ecosystem. If you think of this energy dynamic as a pyramid (see diagram), with a few large, meat-eating animals up at the top and a multitude of tiny floating plants at the base, you can see just what Theme II means.

Activity 1: Who Eats Who?

Objective: To demonstrate a typical marine (ocean) food web.

Time: One period.

Materials: A ball of string or rope (about 30 feet or so)
Extra lengths of thin string
5x8-inch cards with the names of various ocean creatures (enough so everyone can play). Sample labels: Sun, plant plankton, animal plankton, baby herring, baby hake, crab, lobster, tern, puffin, gull, eider duck, mussel, seal, Minke whale, etc.
Recommended number of players: 10-20

Method: Have students stand in a circle. Loop a length of string through each card and hang it from a child's neck, so that each child is tagged with a card. Tell the students that they're going to show what a simple version of the web of life looks like. Each student will soon be challenged to come up with a simple explanation of how his or her organism is connected with another.

Give one end of the string to a student and have him or her toss the ball to another person. Then ask him/her to explain their relationship (we're assuming some amount of preparation beforehand!). For example: Baby hake to animal plankton: "I eat animal plankton!" Or a mussel to the sun: "The sun gives energy to the plant plankton, which I eat." Students may need help in teasing out these relationships, especially if they're young or haven't studied this before. As the ball of string is passed from one person to the other, the food web takes shape.

When everyone is included, announce that a disease has struck the herring, or a tanker has spilled oil. Then have the affected students tug on their string (i.e.,the herring or a plankton). Others will feel the pulling too. This, of course, shows the interdependency of life in a simplistic way. Try removing one member, and see what happens.

Undo the web and discuss. You can also ask students to draw the web.

The Food Chain Game

LUCY GAGLIARDO

Activity 2: Food Chain Mobiles

Objective: Using simple materials, each student crafts a mobile showing three or four feeding relationships.

Time: One to one and a half periods.

Materials: Oaktag or sturdy paper
Compasses
Pencils
Paints, crayons, or felt-tip pens
Thin string or sewing thread.

Methods: Students draw a life-sized puffin, tern, or other seabird shape on oaktag and then a smaller-sized fish. They cut out these shapes. A large circle is cut out in the puffin's mid-section where the fish will hang. Using coloring pens, etc., students finish their creations, making sure to do both sides. But save a space on the fish, and draw in its stomach, showing plankton inside.

Punch a small hole in the puffin's body above the open circle and string the fish's line

Two Food Chain Mobiles

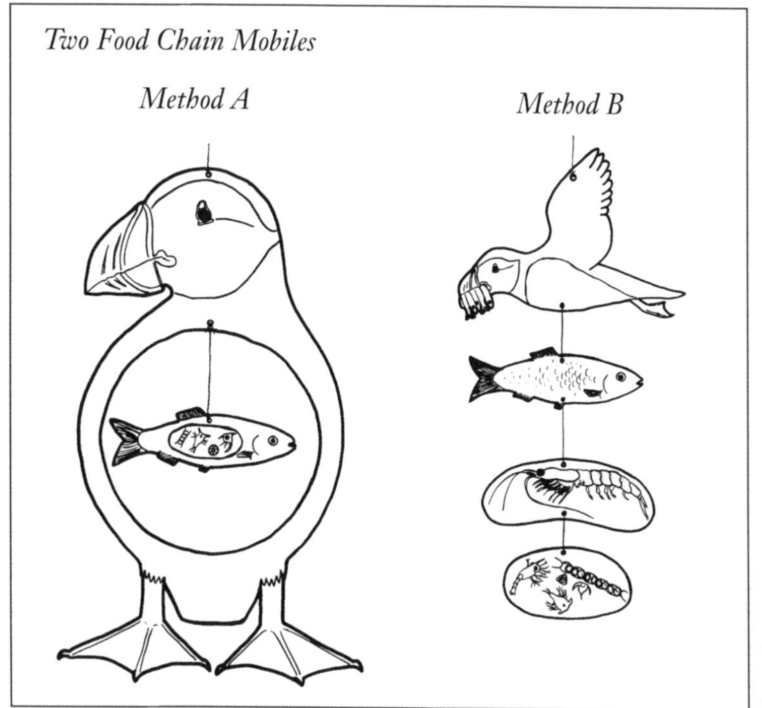

LUCY GAGLIARDO

through, and tie. The fish should dangle freely. Punch another hole in the top of the puffin, and hang it up for display.

Method B uses one more cutout and a vertical design. Instead of cutting out a hole inside the puffin, leave it whole and string the fish directly below it. Then have kids cut out the shape of a smaller fish or a shrimp, color it on both sides, and hang it below the fish.

PHOTO BY STEVE KRESS

Activity 3: Food Chain Game*

Objective: Students will "become" one of three animals in a marine food chain and will try to eat their prey while attempting to survive. Feeding relationships will be observed. Ten or more students are needed to play. (Note: This is an *active* game best held outside or in a large indoor space. For a class of 25 students, use an area at least as big as a full-sized basketball court.) This game can be very fast, and the teacher needs to keep a close and analytical eye on what's happening in order to know which changes will work best in succeeding rounds.

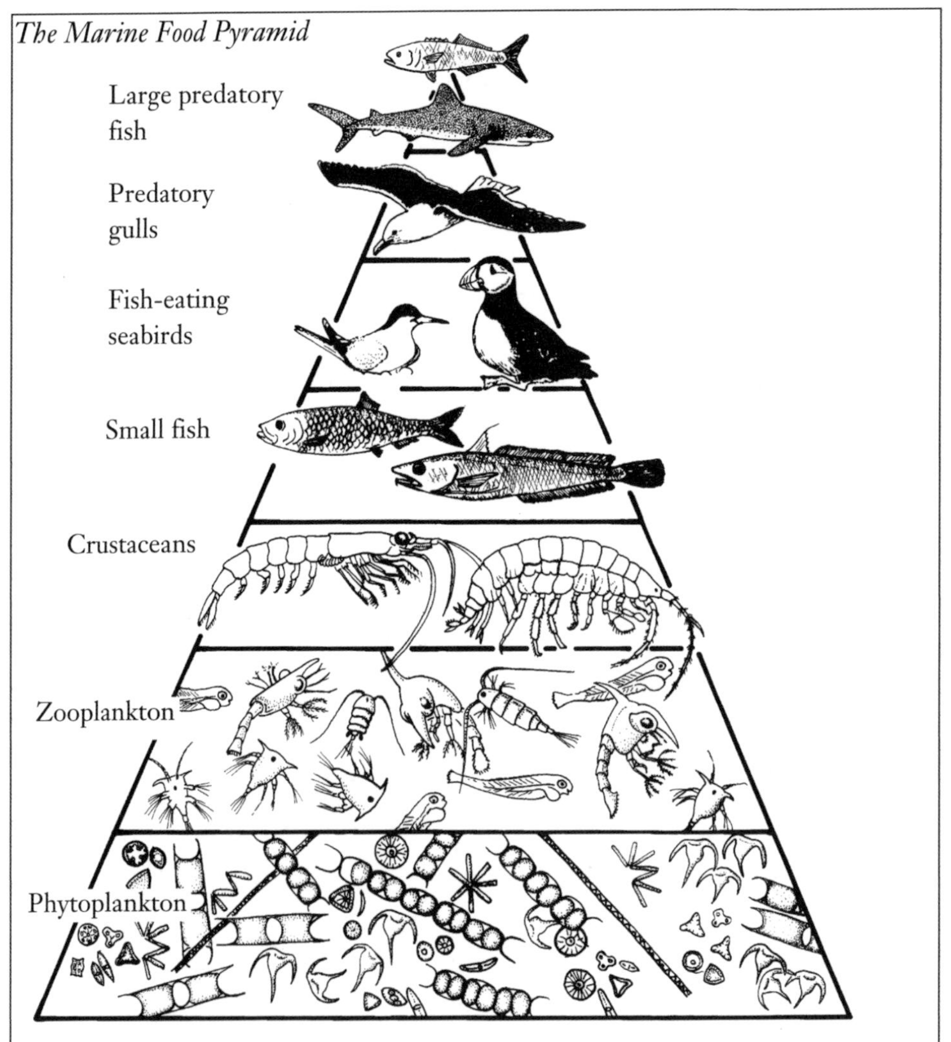

The Marine Food Pyramid

LUCY GAGLIARDO

Time: At least one period. Another period or two for graphing results.

Materials: Six to eight quarts of popped corn

Several dozen Zip-loc plastic sandwich bags

A one-inch-wide roll of masking tape

Colored sashes, one yard long and an inch or two wide (enough for all players) in three different colors (the following colors are just suggestions), about 60% green, 35% blue, 35% red. You could make these sashes from plastic flagging (there will need to be extras).

A wristwatch

Data board

Marker

Material Preparation: The plastic bags will function as "stomachs." Place a strip of masking tape across the bag so the bottom edge of the tape is $1^1/_2$ inches from the bottom of the bag. Also set the boundaries for the playing area.

Introduction to Students/Beginning the Game:

If you conducted the previous activity, "Who Eats Who," students will know about members of marine food webs. If not, you may want to briefly go over the concept. Introduce this new game by diagraming on the board the following: plant plankton——animal plankton——young herring——puffins.

Explain that this is a typical, though simplified, food chain. (Can they think of others, for example, in a field or a forest?) This particular feeding relationship needs to be clear to all your students before you begin.

Tell them they are going to play a tag game where each person will play one member in the food chain. (To avoid popularity contests, you may want to assign roles by drawing numbers.) Each animal will try to get something to eat without being eaten itself (except the puffins) before the "hour" (five minutes) is over.

Show the limits of the game area. (Either beforehand or at this time spread out the popcorn over the playing field.) Tell the group that the popcorn represents tiny floating plants called phyto or plant plankton. These make food in their bodies by using the sun's energy plus oxygen, carbon dioxide, and water. They are the foundation for the entire world ocean food web.

Hand out a plastic bag and a green sash (animal plankton) to a third of your students. Tell these children to store their food (popcorn) in their stomachs (plastic bags) once the game begins.

Hand out a plastic bag and a blue sash (herring) to another third of your group, and red sashes (puffins) and bags to the last third, with similar instructions.

When the game begins, herring will try to capture, or tag, animal plankton, and puffins will try to tag the herring. When a herring tags an animal plankton, they get the food (popcorn) in that zooplankton's bag. When a puffin tags a herring it, too, gets its food. Puffins do not pursue animal plankton, however, only herring.

Tell the kids that during the first round they have five minutes. Yell "Go!" This first round usually lasts only a few seconds with one of two things happening. Animal plankton are gobbled up before they have a chance to feed, or the herring are eaten and the plankton continue to eat popcorn and get fat. Tell students that the next rounds will last longer once you make the changes necessary to "balance" the system.

How many animals survived? For an animal plankton to survive, popcorn must fill the stomach bag to the bottom of the tape ($1\frac{1}{2}$ inches high). For a herring to survive, popcorn must fill the stomach bag to the top of the tape ($2\frac{1}{2}$ inches high.) Puffins must have the equivalent of two herring to survive. If at least one of each kind of animal survives, you have an ongoing food chain. Return the popcorn to the activity area and go to succeeding rounds.

Continuing the Game/Making Adjustments:
The class has an opportunity to learn by making rule variations. Ask for suggestions on rule changes that might result in more of a balance. Typically, one rule is changed for each replay, but you can do two changes if pressed for time. When you have settled on new rules, play again. Suggest these if the students don't offer appropriate ones:

- Change the number of animal plankton and/or herring and/or puffins. For example, try 60% plankton, 20% herring, and 20% puffins, or variations on that theme.
- Let each plankton come back one more time as another plankton, after being tagged and transferring his/her popcorn.
- Provide a safety zone for plankton and/or herring where they can be safe. What about a time limit for staying there?
- Try timed releases. Let the plankton go first to feed unmolested. One minute later release the herring, and in another, release the puffins.
- Use more popcorn.

Remember, one goal of the game is to see if you can balance the system!

Ending the Game/Discussion and Analyzing the Results:
After each game analyze the results. How many plankton got a full stomach? How many herring? How many puffins?

Encourage your students to compare game results after each rule change, and to comment on how the game "balance" compares with balance in the real world. In nature, there are more plants than plant eaters and more plant eaters than meat eaters. You might wish to graph the different game results on the board or as a followup activity.

Analysis questions to consider:

- What would happen with only half as much popcorn (plant plankton)? What could happen to the animals dependent on this? If there were no herring, what would happen to the plant plankton population? To the animal plankton population? To the puffin population?
- Do puffins need plants to survive? Why?
- What food chains are humans part of?
- Are there any plants or animals that are not part of any food chains?
- What about gulls? What would happen if we had a few gulls in the game preying on puffins? How might that change things?

Note: In nature the populations of plants and animals are usually large enough to ensure continuation of the species if some are lost. In this game populations of animal plankton, herring, and puffins are so small that the survival of even one or two of each kind will be considered an indication of an ongoing "balanced" community.

*This activity has been adapted, with permission, from the University of California's Outdoor Biological Instructional Strategies (OBIS) program, devised at the Lawrence Hall of Science.

Activity 4: Examining Plankton Under a Microscope

Objective: To allow students a glimpse into the microscopic world of the all-important plankton community.

Time: One or two periods.

Materials: Artistic renditions or photographs of typical forms of phyto and zoo plankton from high school or biology texts

Dissecting microscopes (perhaps one for every two or three children would be ideal, but any number is fine). If you can't get individual microscopes, perhaps you can get a projecting microscope which shows the image against a screen.

Slides

A plankton sample. You can catch your own sample in a pond or in the ocean with a plankton net, or you can buy a prepared slides from a biological supply house such as Carolina (see below).

Methods: Familiarize the students with some typical plankton forms such as desmids and diatoms. Then show them how to correctly prepare a slide, and how to use the scope. Give them time to discover a variety of life, and then ask them to each draw one or two they find interesting.

Activity 5: Upwellings

Objective: To demonstrate two types of upwellings, and how they bring bottom nutrients towards the surface.

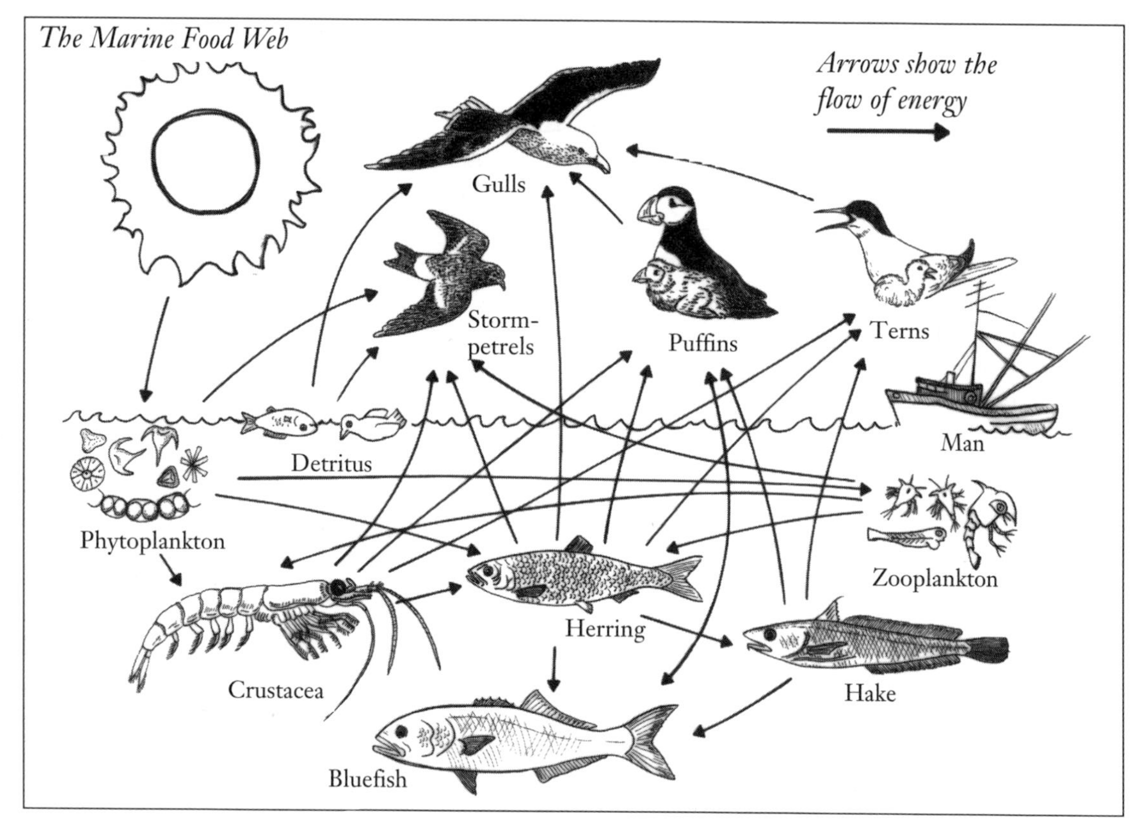

Time: Half a period, after setup.

Materials: A ten-gallon or larger aquarium
Two aquarium hoses (three feet long or longer, 1/4 inch diameter or more)
Two large funnels
Two one-quart or half-gallon plastic jugs
Red and green vegetable dye
A few handfuls of sand
A rock the size of a grapefruit or larger, or a pile of smaller rocks equal to that size

Method: Fill aquarium about half full with water. Put sand on the bottom in the middle. Fill one jug with lightly colored red water and the other one with lightly colored green water. Place the funnels in one end of each hose and place the other end of each hose along the bottom of the tank, opposite each other, from one to twelve inches apart (experiment!). Have two students pour the colored waters into the funnels at the same time and then watch what happens. Discuss.

Clean out the tank and fill again halfway with clean water. Put the rock in the middle of the tank bottom and spread the sand around it. Repeat procedure with hoses and colored water, only this time aim the hose ends at the sides of the rock. What happens? Discuss.

Discussion: Upwellings are one extremely important mechanism for the redistribution of nutrients within a marine ecosystem. When one current hits another, such as the Labrador current meeting the Gulf Stream off Newfoundland, or when one current hits an underwater bank such as at George's Bank off the Maine coast, sediments and nutrients at the bottom are raised and are thus made accessible to phytoplankton (tiny floating plants) such as diatoms. This "fertilizer" allows for a great increase in metabolism and growth to take place. (Upwellings also occur where there are temperature differences in converging currents.)

At upwelling areas then, there are great plankton blooms. Zooplankton feed on the phytoplankton, increase themselves in huge numbers, thus benefiting the entire food web. Fish, seabirds, and marine mammals congregate in these areas to feed. Stellwagen Bank, off Cape Cod, Massachusetts, is one such location and is an excellent place to see whales and other wildlife.

Bibliography

Kids Books:

Doris, Ellen. *Marine Biology*. Thames and Hudson, 1993. Part of the "Children's School of Science" series. Kids go on a whale watch, visit a saltmarsh estuary, etc.

Macquitty, Miranda. *Ocean*. Eyewitness Books, Knopf, 1995. As with the other books in this highly popular series, the layout and photographs are excellent but the text may be beyond many third to sixth graders.

Morris, Rick. *Mysteries and Marvels of Ocean Life*. Usborne, 1983. Very readable, with good graphics.

Parker, Steve. *Seashore*. Eyewitness Books, Knopf, 1989. See comments for other books in the Eyewitness series. (Macquitty, above)

Wade, Larry. *Whales in the Classroom: Volume I Oceanography*. Singing Rock Press, 1992. A good workbook/text covering basic oceanography; written for upper elementary school students.

Wells, Susan. *The Illustrated World Of Oceans*. Simon and Schuster, 1991. Colorfully and plentifully illustrated, this introduction to the world's oceans covers many topics, including physical factors, exploration, sea legends, diversity of life, and man's impact. The layout holds one's interest.

Adult Books:

Coulombe, Deborah. *The Seaside Naturalist*. Simon and Schuster, 1984. Simple drawings, lots of information. Includes a chapter on seabirds. Has a true or false test for each chapter.

National Wildlife Federation. *Diving into Oceans*. A Naturescope Activity Guide, 1988. A good source of activities and basic information.

Internet Resources:

Facts About Birds: The Food Chain/Food Web.
http:llwww.nceet.snre.umich.edu/Curriculum/birdfacts.html

Ocean Planet—Smithsonian
Includes teacher materials, lesson plans, and fact sheets.
http://seawifs.gsfc.nasa.gov/OCEAN_PLANET/HTML/search_educational_materials.html

Other Resources:

Carolina Biological Supply Company, 2700 York Road, Burlington, NC 27215. (919) 584-0381.

M.A.R.E., Lawrence Hall of Science, University of California at Berkeley, California. A whole-school, K-8 multicultural science program of ocean study activities.

Marine Mammal Commission, 1825 Connecticut Avenue N.W., Washington, DC 20009. offers a free booklet about sea mammals and an endangered species coloring book.

National Marine Fisheries Service, c/o SHPI, Rm 12727, Silver Spring Metro Center 3, 1315 East West Highway, Silver Spring, MD 20910. Offers a free color fact poster entitled "Earth is a Marine Habitat." Send SASE.

National Oceanic and Atmospheric Administration, Public Affairs Correspondence Unit, 1305 East West Highway, 8624, Silver Spring, MD. 20910. Offers a free fact sheet about sea turtles, and a marine debris coloring book.

Theme III: Birds and Wildlife in North America Have Suffered Because of Man's Depredations Over Past Centuries

Introduction

In North America, from 1600 to 1900, wildlife was hunted without relief. By the turn of the last century many populations had been decimated. From an estimated 60 million bison only a thousand or so were left. Billions of Passenger Pigeons once graced our skies and woodlands but were pursued to extinction by 1914. And puffins, which once nested on five U.S.-owned islands in the Gulf of Maine, were reduced to only two pairs by 1901.

Motivations in those earlier years were a mixture of hunting for food, hunting for a willing and ever-expanding market, and, sadly, a devastating lack of respect for other forms of life. But voices were raised, meetings were called, and laws were passed. Destructive businesses such as the feather trade and market hunting were eventually stopped. In recent years much important legislation, consciousness-raising, and education have done wonders here in America for both humans and wildlife.

As an educator it's extremely important not to convey to children feelings of hopelessness or powerlessness. It is important to be honest about the facts, and hopeful about each person's ability to contribute positively towards a better world. Children may mourn the story of the Great Auk's demise, and that of other ravaged species. Hear them out. Listen. Affirm their right to have feelings and opinions. And move towards harnessing this energy and power towards individual and collective action. There are plenty of animals and habitats that need our attention now (see Theme VII).

Activity 1: Role-Playing

Objective: To give students an exciting and fresh perspective on events of the past, thus illuminating the present as well.

Time: Varies.

Methods: These role-playing dramas can take the form of a town meeting, a debate, or mini-theater. Present the class with different scenarios, give them background information or show them where they can find research materials, and coach them on how to prepare for their individual roles. The teacher acts as a moderator or facilitator of the action. Have other members of the class be ready to discuss some of the issues that came up during the role-playing event.

Scenario A: The Feather Trade

It's a legislative hearing in the year 1898 in the state of Maine. One side wants the government to pass a law stopping the killing of birds for their feathers. These folks are: Several lighthouse keepers who live on seabird islands, members of the Portland Natural History Society, representatives of the Bird Protection Committee of the American Ornithologist's Union, and local citizens who love wildlife.

The other side does not want a law passed. Among them are: Hat makers, fashion designers, hunters, feather processors, and shop owners. They are concerned with holding on to their jobs.

What parallels do you see with current events? For instance, the Spotted Owl v. timber industry concerns in the Pacific Northwest. The cod and flounder fishery?

Scenario B: The Passenger Pigeon

Your class is on a field trip to the Cincinnati Zoo in the year 1913. The last surviving Passenger Pigeon, named Martha, is in her cage (she later died in 1914). Your class hears a panel discussion from zoo biologists who tell you the whole story of how the Passenger Pigeons happened to meet their tragic fate.

Later on you travel to a Fish and Game Club to talk with a group of men who were professional pigeon hunters. They tell you their story.

(The children can prepare for this, or the other scenarios by writing scripts which they can read at the staged event. You might consider using costumes or props, as well.)

Scenario C: Confronting the Eggers

(This may be easier for younger students to act out—they don't have to do much background preparation.) Your family has taken a Sunday picnic to an island somewhere off the coast. The year is 1885. You come upon a group of people who are in the process of collecting hundreds of seabird eggs—directly from the active nests of gulls, terns, and eider ducks. You know the colony has been declining in size for years. The eggers want food and want to sell eggs at market.

Explore the parallel to the present-day practice in some tropical areas of collecting turtle eggs.

Scenario D: A Walk on the Beach

It's August or September a hundred years ago. A group of young people and their teacher/leader are walking on the beach to see the hundreds, if not thousands, of migrating shorebirds that have landed here to feed along the mudflats and rest during their long, annual journey from the subarctic to the tropics. Suddenly three or four dogs appear and begin wildly chasing the birds. The birds fly off. The dogs go back to some people having a picnic above the high tide zone. Your group is upset at seeing how the dogs disturbed the birds. You decide to go up to the picnickers and explain why the birds need to be able to carry out their feeding and resting. Could they please keep their dogs on leashes? (Teachers: This is a drama that still happens all too often today.)

Scenario E: Modern-Day Decision-Making

A group of scientists is interested in re-establishing a colony of Atlantic Puffins on a former breeding island. That seven-acre island, however, is home to 200 pair of Great Back-blacked and Herring Gulls, which are known predators of puffins. The gulls nest in the grass near the rocky crevices that puffins would use as their burrow sites. To successfully re-introduce puffins, the scientists will have to destroy most of the breeding gulls and break up eggs they find in the nest. This may have to be done for the next two years to make sure all, or almost all, of the gulls with a sense of territoriality are elminated. Many methods other than poisoning (scarecrows, noise, a moving scarecrow, etc.) have been tried in the past at different sites, but none has worked.

The poison is applied to bread and margarine cubes, which are placed in each gull's nest. When a gull eats the bread, it dies of kidney failure within three days; the poison does not affect the gull's nervous system. No other animal or bird on the island eats bread, and because the poison itself breaks down within a few hours, there is little chance of poisoning scavenging animals that might feed on dead gulls.

Animal rights activists do not want this plan to go forward, and they will work to stop it. They don't believe in killing one species of animal to make way for another, even if one population greatly dominates the other, and even if humans are responsible for the dramatic rise in gull numbers due to abundant food sources from our garbage dumps and from the fishing industry.

Have the students divide into the two interest groups, research and discuss their positions, and then present their ideas and reasoning to the class. (See below for some facts and opinions related to this issue.) When both sides have had a chance to finish their debate and answer questions, call for a class vote. Should gulls be destroyed on this particular island to make way for a puffin restoration effort? Discuss the final results.

Facts to consider in favor of gull control:

- Gulls nest on 242 Maine islands.
- Puffins nest on only one other Maine island at this time. (In the early 1970s, when National Audubon Society was faced with this issue, puffins nested only on Matinicus Rock.)
- Great Black-backed Gull numbers have been increasing for 70 years.
- Puffins first disappeared because of hunting. Now gulls prevent them from returning on their own.
- If restoration works for puffins, it could be good news for all colonial-nesting seabirds; 10% of worldwide species are at risk of extinction.
- Puffin restoration could spur on local eco-tourism businesses.
- (Opinion) People have an ethical responsibility to act as stewards for all species. We must not, therefore, let any species go extinct if we can help it.

Arguments against gull control:

- People should not kill animals for any reason.
- People should not make animals suffer by poisoning them.
- People should not "tinker" with the so-called "balance of nature."
- It is wrong to "play God" by favoring one species over another.
- Poisons can have unexpected results when used in nature.

Activity 2: The Ups and Downs of Island Seabird Colonies.

Objective: By using graphs, students will see how populations of terns, gulls, and other birds have changed over the past century.

Time: Varies

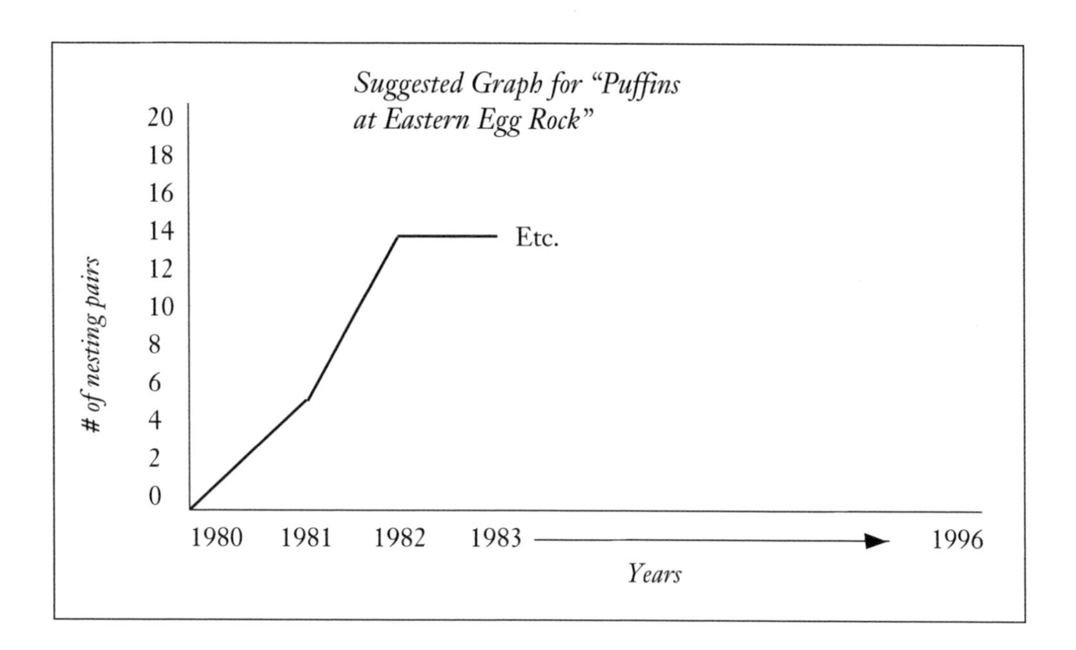

Graph A: Puffins at Eastern Egg Rock

1887—zero, 1980—zero, 1981—5 pairs, 1982—14 pairs, 1983—14 pairs, 1984—14 pairs, 1985—20 pairs, 1986—19 pairs, 1987—18 pairs, 1988—16 pairs, 1989—14 pairs, 1990—15 pairs, 1991—16 pairs, 1992—16 pairs,
1993—15 pairs, 1994—15 pairs, 1995—16 pairs, 1996—19 pairs.

Graph B: Terns at Matinicus Rock* (*similar setup, same X and Y axis as Puffin graph)*

1936—3,000 pairs, 1979 —612 pairs, 1984—760 pairs, 1986 —774 pairs, 1988—1,000 pairs, 1990—1,250 pairs, 1995—1,237 pairs, 1996—1,013 pairs.

* We believe the decline in tern numbers from the 1930s to the 1970s was caused by the great increase in the regional gull population. Gulls use similar nesting areas, arrive there earlier than the highly migratory terns, and will harass terns and eat eggs and young. Gull control began on Matinicus Rock in 1971, thus allowing the return and safety of greater numbers of nesting terns.

Graph C: Herring Gull Populations:

In 1901—11,000 pairs on 17 New England islands
In 1931—26,000 pairs on 65 New England islands
In 1977—88,500 pairs on 379 New England islands
In 1985—96,803 pairs on 383 New England islands

Graph D: Great Black-Backed Gull Populations:

pre-1883: Eliminated from the New England coast. Previous numbers unknown.
1928—First colonies naturally re-established on Maine coast, 25 to 35 pairs.
1940s—1,700 pairs on Maine islands
1972—7,500 pairs on Maine islands
1977—9,850 pairs on Maine islands. (And 20,450 pairs on 297 islands from Long Island to the Canadian border.)

Gull Populations:
Either use two graphs for each species as follows...

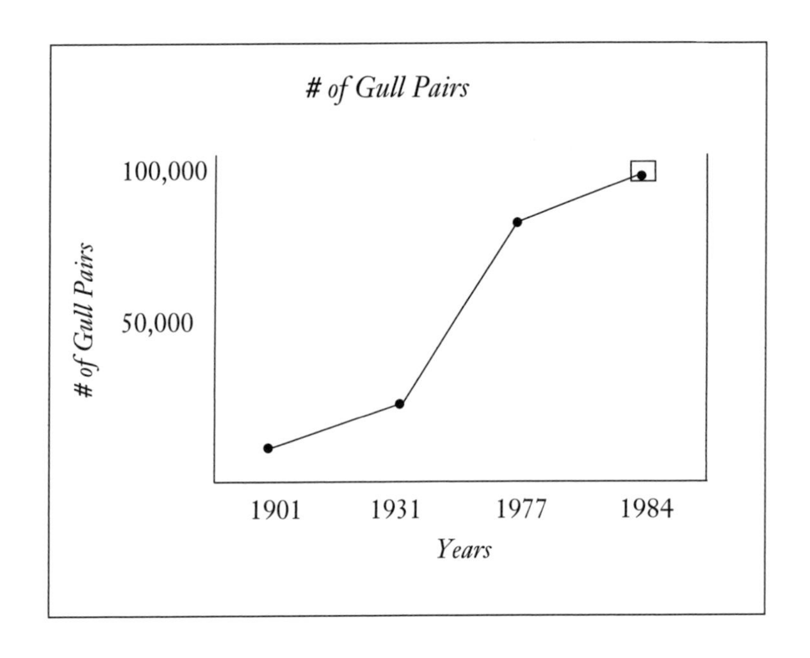

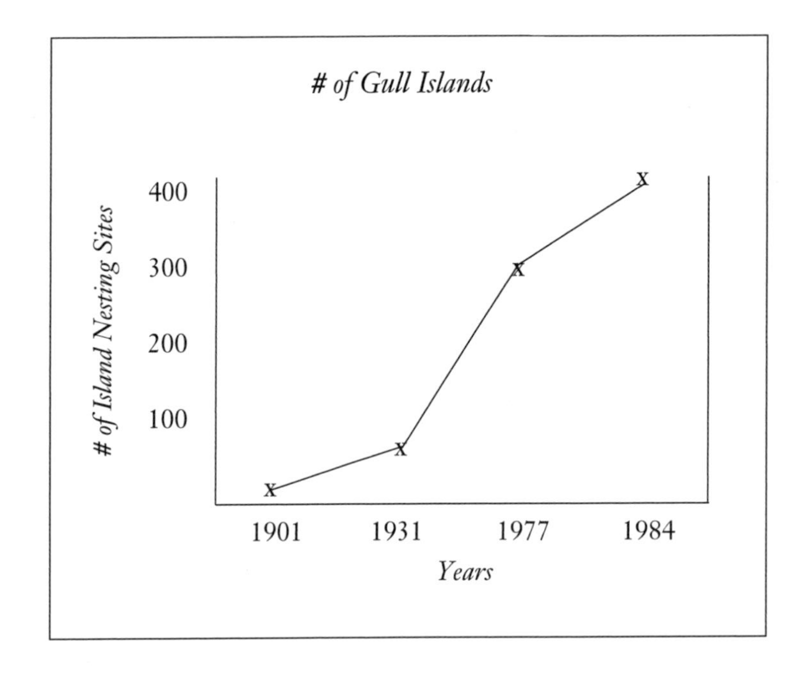

...or use one overlay graph with 2 "Y" axes for each species

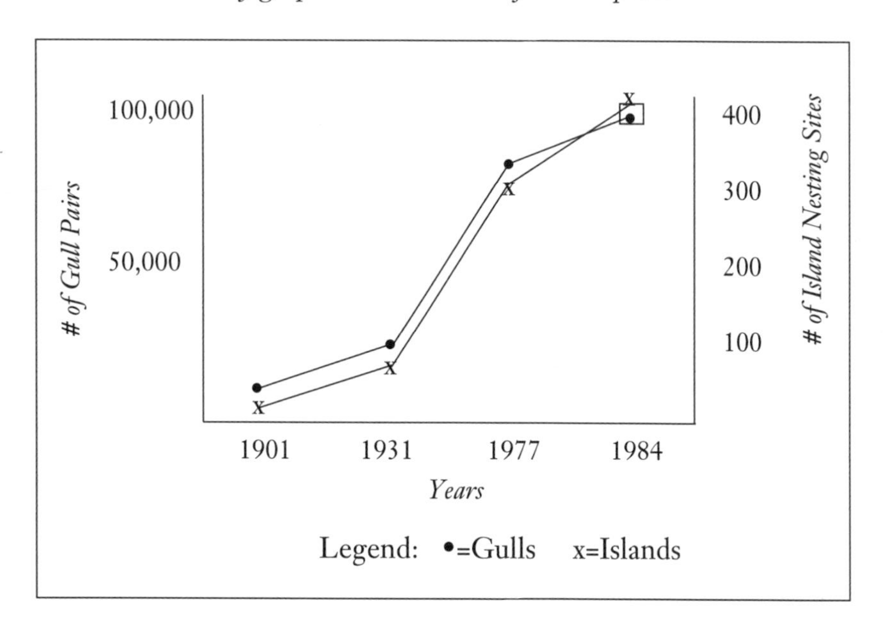

Activity 3: What Can You Learn About Animals in Trouble?

Objective: Students will study different animals that suffered years ago (bison, great auk, eskimo curlew, etc) and compare them with animals in trouble now (sea turtles, Siberian Tigers, rhinos, gorillas, etc.)

Time: Half period in class, with more time for library research.

Materials: Photos or drawings of animals that suffered their greatest depredations years ago (bison, Passenger Pigeon, Great Auk, tern, wolf, Ivory-billed Woodpecker). The same for animals *now* having trouble (sea turtles, Peregrine Falcon, Black-footed Ferret, Grizzly Bear, Spotted Salamander). Papers for posting on board or wall with *individual reasons* written on them why these animals suffered at the hands of man. (Loss of habitat and other factors also played a part, but these are the primary reasons.)

Reasons are as follows:

- Bison—hunted for its meat and fur
- Passenger Pigeon—hunted for its meat
- Great Auk—hunted for its meat
- Tern—hunted for its feathers
- Wolf—killed for its fur, and, people were afraid of it.
- Ivory-billed Woodpecker—loss of habitat

Modern examples:

- Sea turtle—caught for its eggs, meat, and products; loss of nesting habitat on southern beaches; caught by commercial fishermen.
- Peregrine Falcon—pesticides (DDT) in its food supply caused eggshell thinning.
- Black-footed Ferret—its food item (prairie dogs) poisoned by livestock ranchers.
- Grizzly Bear—habitat loss, killed because people were afraid of it.
- Spotted Salamander—acid rain kills its eggs and larvae.

Methods: Students research individual animals, both past and present, and share their findings with the class. Then this activity takes the form of a matching game. Students try to match the photos of animals with cards telling the various reasons why these specific creatures suffered or are suffering. Hang or post the first group of photos in one area, and the second in another. Do the same with the reason cards. Students walk around, looking, writing down names of animals and the reasons why they suffered. Let them consult with each other. Give them about 10 minutes.

Discussion: Hunting for food and products was the main reason animals were killed and threatened with extinction years ago. Modern-day animals face a far greater array of threats. Why have animals been persecuted? What are their habitats (past and present), food sources, present situations, etc.? (See Theme IV for more on this.)

Activity 4: The Great Auk

Objective: For students to find out how the Great Auk became extinct, and what lessons might be drawn from the past for present day concerns.

Time: One hour to view the film, one period or more to discuss and follow up.

Materials: NOVA documentary video entitled *The Haunted Cry of a Long Gone Bird*. Call 1-800-255-9424. ($19.95)

Background Discussion: Dick Wheeler, a retired teacher and naturalist, traces the 1,700-mile former migration route (from Newfoundland to Cape Cod Bay) of the Great Auk during his solo kayak adventure of 1991. The Great Auk once nested in large numbers along the northeast coast, especially off Newfoundland, but was hunted by sailors and feather traders until the last ones disappeared in 1844. A followup educational program to the NOVA film is called the "Great Auk Project," and is a creation of educators at the National Estuarine Sanctuary at Stellwagen Bank, 14 Union Street, Plymouth, MA 02360.

Bibliography

Kids Books:

Godkin, Celia. *Wolf Island*. Fitzhenry & Whiteside, 1989. When a wolf population is accidentally removed from its island habitat, the natural food chain is disrupted. An information guide is available.

———. *Sea Otter Bay*. Fitzhenry & Whiteside, 1997. Another picture book exploring the delicate balance of a natural ecosystem. Also has an information guide.

Jeffers, Susan. *Brother Eagle, Sister Sky: A Message from Chief Seattle*. Dial, 1991. The text is adapted from the alleged words of Chief Seattle, who speaks eloquently of understanding and respect for the earth and its creatures. Lovely artwork.

McClung, Robert. *Lost Wild America*. Linnet Books, 1993. A comprehensive and historical view of the interaction between wildlife and humans in North America. Easy to read. Pen and ink drawings. Many specific species accounts. For fifth grade up through middle school.

Lasky, Kathryn, *She's Wearing a Dead Bird On Her Head!* Hyperion, 1995. A colorful, humorous, and essentially true story of how two women in late 19th-century Boston decided to try to end the fashionable practice of displaying birds and feathers on ladies' hats. Their efforts also led to the formation of the Massachusetts Audubon Society in 1895.

Internet Resources:

Facts About Birds: Basic Needs of Birds, Birds as Environmental Indicators, Factors in Contemporary Society Affecting Birds, Moves to Counteract Conditions that Adversely Affect Birds.
http:llwww.nceet.snre.umich.edu/Curriculum/birdfacts.html

Wolf Studies, International Wolf Center.
http://wolf.org

The Peregrine Fund
http://peregrinefund.org/IntroPF.html

Meet the California Condor
http://edf.org/species/pages/condor.html

California Condor Restoration
http://www.peregrinefund.org.CACondor.html

The Black-Footed Ferret
Information at
http://bluegoose.arw.r0fus.gov/NWRSFiles/WildlifeMgmt/SpeciesAccounts/Mammals/BlackFootedFerret.html
Photo at
http://www.bhm.tis.net/zoo/ao/mammal/bfferret.htm

Extinction or Survival Game
http:llwww.bvis.uic.edu/museum/exhibits/lot_media/games/Extinct.html

Theme IV: Current Human Impacts Threaten Marine Ecosystems

Introduction

You've heard the old admonition, "Don't put all your eggs in one basket." Seventy-one percent of all the puffins in North America are concentrated in Newfoundland's Witless Bay. In today's world, this phenomenon makes for a potentially dangerous situation. What if an oil tanker were to break apart there during breeding season? What might happen to any large seabird colony in the event of a local pollution catastrophe?

Of course, many threats to puffins and seabirds are less "spectacular." Consider what happens when people overfish for herring and other seabird foods. Or when non-discriminating gill nets, which hang from the ocean's surface like an invisible curtain of death, are spread near a colony of diving birds. Chemical spills and toxics are also a threat, as are plastics and other litter tossed at sea. And the introduction of mammals, such as rats or cats, to a seabird island is always devastating. (Our work in the Galapagos Islands helping to restore the globally endangered Dark-rumped Petrel was necessary because of this very reason—rats, dogs, and other introduced species had decimated the bird colonies.)

(Activities in Themes V and VII stress the positive approaches human beings are taking, and we believe they will serve as a balance to this section.)

Activity 1: Everybody Wants a Fish Dinner/Tragedy of the Commons*

(Suggested for older students)

Objective: Students will participate in a simulation game, harvesting fish from an area held in common by all nations. They will make decisions regarding their harvesting which may lead to fish extinction. They will analyze their experiences and learn more about the dynamics that drive this "tragedy of the commons." They will come to understand the concept of "carrying capacity."

Time: Three 45-minute periods (one for the game, two for followup)

Materials: 600 paper clips or toothpicks (these are the fish). Poster board or large paper, for charts

Advance Preparation: Find an area about 150 feet on a side. A mowed lawn or a field is recommended, but an area of blacktop, a gymnasium, or a large multi-purpose room will be suitable. Randomly scatter the paper clips or toothpicks over the area. Make a chart for recording your results (see illustration). Divide the class into four equal groups.

Instructions to the Teacher and Students for Playing the Game:

1. Let each group choose a name for the country it represents. Tell them they will be fishing in waters that are shared by all nations and that the economic livelihood of their countries depends on fishing.
2. Put each group in one corner of the playing area, which represents the common waters.

Chart for "Everybody Wants a Fish Dinner"

	Round 1	Round 2	Round 3	Round 4	Round 5
Country 1	% of fish harvested / $$ Profit				
Country 2					
Country 3					
Country 4					

Each group is allowed to send one "boat" (person) in the first "year" (one minute) to harvest the fish (paper clips). Each group needs to harvest ten fish per year to feed the people in its country. Each additional fish can be sold for a profit and is worth $2.

3. Begin the first round by letting each country send one boat into the playing area to collect fish. At the end of one minute yell "stop." Ask the boats to return to their home port and count their fish. The students should put their fish in groups of ten. Ask each group to tell you how many fish it caught. Record this number on the chart.
4. Tell the students to subtract the ten fish their country needs to feed its population from the total number of fish they collected. If a country catches fewer than ten fish, the country is in distress and one student in the group must sit out the remaining rounds to represent a declining population and a smaller work force. If a country catches more than ten fish, the extra fish are each worth $2 towards the purchase of additional boats. The countries may buy more boats (active fishermen) for $20 apiece. Once a group purchases the boats it needs, the remaining fish become the country's profit. Record each country's profit.
5. Ask the students to use the chart to calculate the number of fish remaining in the water from the original 600. Tell students these fish can reproduce, and their reproduction rate is one-half the remaining fish. Return the correct number of paper clips to the playing area, collecting the number you need from the group's piles. (For example, if more than 400 fish remain, return all the paper clips to the playing area. If 300 fish remain, return 150 fish to the playing area, making a total of 450 fish available for harvest in the second round. Collect and set aside any extra paper clips.
6. Begin the second round of fishing, allowing the new boats (students) to leave each group with the original boat (you can switch students so everyone gets a chance to play). After one minute, ask each group to count its fish, feed its country, buy additional boats (up to the number of people in the group), and record its profit. Calculate the number of fish to

return to the water, as in Step 5, and throw the correct number of paper clips onto the playing area.

7. Continue to fish in one-minute rounds. When the students have depleted, or nearly depleted the fish population the simulation game is over. Gather your class together and ask the following questions as you discuss the results of the students' fishing expeditions:

- Which country was most profitable in its fishing excursions?
- What happened to the number of paper clips the student collected as fishing continued?
- If the goal was not to make money but to sustain themselves on Earth for the longest time, did anyone win?
- What could the students have done to sustain the fish population?

Understanding the Concept of the "Tragedy of the Commons":

In 1968 Garrett Hardin wrote a paper entitled "Tragedy of the Commons." In this classic work, Hardin described the way common areas fall victim to tragedy: individuals who share the commons try to increase their "take." Individuals are compelled to continue such action because the positive consequences for the individual (profit) far exceeds the negative consequences (degradation of the commons). The rational conclusion drawn by each individual is therefore the same: to increase profit without limit, in a world that is, of course, limited.

1. Ask the students how the fishing activity is a "tragedy of the commons." What was the commons in the activity? What is the tragedy? Help the students understand that the "fishing" area represented an environment common to all countries. Each group wanted to harvest as many fish as possible. As time passed the fish became scarcer, and the commons supported fewer healthy countries. Eventually the fish in the commons were near-extinct, and the fishing countries were forced to look elsewhere for fish. Help the students graph the number of fish their team caught each minute, plotted against the time, to illustrate the law of diminishing returns. Remind the students that as time passes, the fishing boats would have to go further, and fish for a longer time, and a smaller yield. (There are frequent articles in newspapers and magazines about this very issue.)
2. Introduce the students to the concept of "carrying capacity." This is defined as the greatest number of individuals of a given species that the environment can support with its available resources. Discuss the carrying capacity of the common waters with respect to fishing countries. Human population is another aspect of this discussion; for example, is the earth past its carrying capacity for the world population of 5.5 billion people?
3. Help the students understand the dynamics and decisions that result in the tragedy of the commons. In the fishing activity, the countries might have cooperated to draw up restrictions on fishing in common waters. Restrictions that benefit a resource, however, may not be in the economic or political interest of an individual or a government in the short term. It is often in a group's short term interest to exploit the resource, even though it may destroy a future livelihood or shared natural resource. What are examples of this? (Clearcutting virgin forests, overgrazing by cattle on public lands, etc.)

Taking Action:

1. Ask the students to identify the commons in their lives. Suggest they consider their house, school, ballpark, national parks, and other public places. What decisions do they make that affect the commons? For example, if they choose to leave picnic litter in a neighborhood park, how does that affect the environment of that commons and the people who share it?
2. Consider writing letters to elected officials about a commons in their neighborhood, state,

country. Ask students to describe it, identify decisions that affect it, and consider the potential of the tragedy of the commons. How might the tragedy be avoided? The students might suggest education, taxes, or rules and restrictions to protect the commons. Encourage the students to ask the officials to make decisions that have positive consequences for the commons, rather than negative ones.

3. Repeat the fishing simulation, but create a new purpose: sustaining the largest number of countries for the longest period of time. Ask students to consider ways to cooperate. Let students divide up the commons, pass restraining laws, or limit profits.
4. Find a current issue to discuss which shows countries of the world cooperating over a common area or resource. For example, Antarctica, outer space, seabed mining, global warming, control of CFC's, etc.

*Permission from the National Science Foundation to use this activity.

Activity 2: A Mountain of Trash*

Objective: Students see how much trash they produce on a daily basis at school. They extrapolate to find out how much trash a 4,000-person Navy ship produces. They're encouraged to figure out alternatives for themselves and for their community. This may lead to a recycling project.

Time: Varies.

Methods: Surprise the students with this activity just before lunch. Ask them to sort, wash, and save all their "garbage." Help figure out where to store it. Continue to do this for one or two weeks. Make bar graphs using different categories, showing increase over each day in total number of items (i.e., number of plastic bags, plastic utensils, cans, jars, lunch bags, napkins, wrappers, etc.) At the end of the week, discuss what could be done to cut down on waste. Using arithmetic, see how much waste a Navy ship produces. Organize an action project to tackle the waste problem in your class/school.

Supplementary Activity: Do a beach/stream/lake cleanup and sort and catalogue what you find. Publicize results!

*Adapted with permission of the Center for Marine Conservation and the California Coastal Commission.

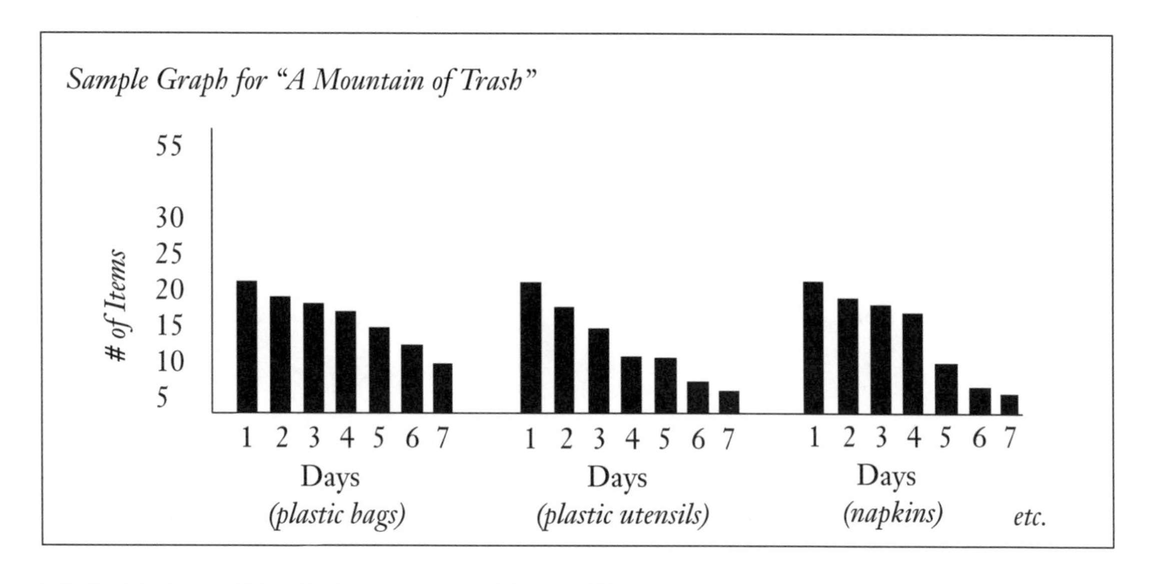

Activity 3: Investigating Water Pollution's Effect on Living Things*

Objective: Students add various "pollutants" to jars holding healthy algae colonies and watch, over time, what the effects are. They see how different substances act in different ways.

Time: Setting up takes the most time, then there will be short periodic observations.

Materials: Four to six quart to half-gallon containers such as canning jars or clear plastic soda bottles
Local pond water, or algae purchased from a biological supply house
Plant fertilizer
Aged tap water
Polaroid camera and film (optional)
Salt
Vinegar
Motor oil
Detergent

Setting Up: It's best to set up the algae colonies about two weeks before adding the pollutants. Fill the jars with aged tap water, or pond water if you have it, and add one teaspoon of plant fertilizer to each. Stir thoroughly. If you've bought algae samples, add equal amounts to the different jars of bottled, spring, or distilled water at this time. Put the jars where they will get good indirect natural light, or under strong incandescent or fluorescent light. Make sure this location is not a cold one.

Your students can be involved in this procedure, and it's a good time to discuss the overall experiment. Explain that you are modeling real ecosystems, and that you wouldn't want to put pollutants in a lake or pond. One jar will serve as your control, and the others will have chemicals added to them.

Once the Mini-Ecosystems Are Ready: Set up two columns on the board, which the students can duplicate in their notebooks: "Point Source Pollution" and "Non-Point Source Pollution." The first means direct pollution, such as a sewer pipe leading into a body of water or an oil spill from a tanker run aground. The second is more widespread and sometimes quite difficult to trace, such as pesticides washing off a farm field during a rainstorm, salt off a road, etc. Ask students to list various pollutants and have them categorize their suggestions. (At a later point you may want to investigate ways to control the different types of pollution.)

Explain how this experiment is going to work, that it will be one of observation over several weeks. Ask students what pollutants they want to add to the jars. Good choices are: vinegar, motor oil, and a strong detergent. Ask them to write down their predictions for what will happen to each jar once the substance is added. Add a reasonable amount, such as a quarter cup or so of vinegar, two tablespoons of a detergent (not green), enough motor

Types of Water Pollution

Point source pollution:	*Non-point source pollution:*
A sewer pipe in the river	Road salt washing off in a rainstorm into a sewer
An oil spill in the bay	Oil from a dump in the backyard, seeping into groundwater
Etc.	Etc.

oil to cover the surface, etc. Make sure you leave one jar untouched; this is your control.

Two or three times a week, have students write down their observations of each mini-ecosystem. Photograph the jars with new labels on them showing the date, every few days.

Results: Some pollutants favor plant growth, while others do not. You may see an algae bloom or a die-off. In the case of motor oil, if the algae can make enough oxygen from sunlight they may be able to stay alive under the oil film. The vinegar, which is acidic, may cause the water to be very clear because it kills the algae. The algae in the control jar should be doing okay.

Finishing Up: You can ask your students to write up the results, with a paragraph explaining what happened for each jar, and how the action compared with their predictions.

Explain that in the ocean much of the life lives near the coast, where there is a nutrient trap from the mixing of fresh and salt waters. If the fresh water is polluted from sources on the land, then the organisms living in the coastal zone will suffer. For example, if a factory disposes of some of its waste products into a river that flows into a bay where puffins have a nesting island, then perhaps the fish populations there will suffer, and consequently, so will the birds.

*Adapted with permission from the Baltimore Aquarium's book *What's In The Water?*

Bibliography

Kids Books:

EarthWorks Press. *50 Simple Things Kids Can Do To Recycle*. EarthWorks, Press, 1994.

Gibbons, Gail. *Recycle: A Handbook for Kids*. Little, Brown and Company, 1002. A behind-the-scenes look at recycling, with helpful tips on how children can help.

Godkin, Celia. *Ladybug Garden*. Fitzhenry & Whiteside, 1995. This story about using pesticides on a garden introduces children to the concept of the balance of nature and natural controls (the ladybug).

Savage, Candace. *Trash Attack*. Douglas and McIntyre, 1990

Adult Books:

Center for Marine Conservation, *A Citizen's Guide to Plastics in the Ocean: More Than A Litter Problem*. Center for Marine Conservation, 1994. Excellent overview and resource guide. Some funny political cartoons (about litter) that students would like.

Internet Resources:

Give Water a Hand: Studying your Watershed, Planning a Project.
http://www.uwex.edu/evc/

Izaak Walton League
Includes information on "The Stream Study"
http://iwla.org/iwla/

Sea World's Teacher's Guide on Water
http://www.bev.net/education/SeaWorld/

Earth Day Classroom Ideas
http://www.cfe.cornell.edu/Earthday/organize/classroom.html

World Wildlife Federation
Information on a variety of subjects, including sustainable fisheries. Kids and Teachers section.
http://www.panda.org

Theme V: Careful Observation and Good Record-Keeping Are Important Tools of Wildlife Biologists

Introduction

Children enjoy playing detective/scientist roles, and they especially like showing off to others what they discover. There are many investigations you can devise that give students the opportunity to learn basic observation and note-taking skills.

You won't have to have your own bird observation blind (though you may want to build one!) nor do you need a laptop computer. But you will need a quiet place from which children can observe, and some paper and pens. Binoculars may also be handy.

Expect the topic of patience to come up, both for you and your students. We suggest you start small, and work on the basics. Bird feeders, bird baths, fast food parking lots, public parks, beaches, and even paved school yards are places you can use as your study sites.

Science Tip: Bird behavior is usually grouped into three large categories: body care; feeding; and social displays. Specific examples of each are as follows:

Body Care: Preening feathers, oiling feathers, bathing in water, bathing in dust, bill-wiping, feather fluffing for warmth, feather settling, stretching, sleeping.

Feeding: Pecking at the ground, at weeds and grasses, on a tree trunk or branch; scratching and pecking in leaves; plucking fruits off twigs; flying after flying insects; probing in the ground or mud.

Social Displays: Singing or calling while sitting or perched, singing or calling while in flight, birds mating, nest building, incubating eggs, feeding young, male or female chasing another bird of the same sex and species to defend territory.

Activity 1: Watching Birds Do Their Thing

Objective: To observe individual birds and to record their various behaviors.

Time: One period or more.

Possible Settings: By windows near bird habitat or feeders, outside in different habitats, at an aviary, aquarium, zoo, or beach.

Materials: A clipboard for each student
- Paper
- Pen
- Watch

Methods: Have kids team up: one will be the recorder and one the observer. Have them pick common species that are more apt to stick around: feeder birds, or house sparrows, starlings, pigeons, mallard ducks, gulls. Children watch birds for a certain period of time (i.e., 5–15 minutes) and write down what the bird does. For example:

Observing Birds
Competition
Some Common
Gull Behaviors
Sleeping
Trumpet Call
Preening
LUCY GAGLIARDO

• 9:25 a.m. Gull is sitting in parking lot and pushing its beak into its side feathers. It plucks at its feathers (preening).
• 9:27 a.m. Gull flies off to side of dumpster and walks around. Puts beak near ground then picks up head. Continues to walk, picks up piece of bread and swallows it. Walks more.
• 9:30 a.m. Gull sits on curb.

When teams get back together they can share what they saw with the others during a wrap-up session. You can tease general questions out of these discussions, and set the stage for further investigations.

Activity 2: More Adventures in Watching Gulls

Objective: To learn more about the behaviors of gulls. Ideally, this will take place at a beach, a field, or wherever gulls may congregate in your area. You may want to go back several times during different seasons of the year or times of the day for comparisons.

Time: One period or more.

Methods: Familiarize your students with note-taking techniques, with using binoculars, and with the differences in adult and juvenile plumages of whatever gull is most common where you are (probably herring, ring-billed, or western). Make up appropriate questions from the list below and give to small teams of observers. One person can serve as observer, another as recorder, etc. Typical worksheet questions are:

1. *Direction and Time of Arrival*
   What time of day and what time of year do gulls come to the area? Do the gulls come in all weather conditions, or only on certain days? What direction(s) do the gulls come from? What other type of habitat might they be using when they are not at the observation site?
2. *Flight Patterns*
   What type of flight pattern or patterns do the gulls follow as they come to the site? Do they fly in a straight line, weave back and forth, rise and fall? Describe the flight and/or draw a picture of the pattern. Do the gulls fly singly or in groups? If they fly in groups, what type of formation do they use?
3. *Favorite Locations on the Site*
   Do the gulls come back to the same spot each time, or do they move around? Why do you think they use some spots more than others?
4. *Specific Behaviors*
   How much of their time do the gulls spend simply resting? Do they have a special resting position (sitting, standing on one leg, etc.)? Do the gulls eat while they visit your site? If so, what do they eat (earthworms, apples, garbage, etc.)? How do they search for the food? If they catch an earthworm, how do they use their bill to handle it? Do they gulls ever seem to fight or argue over food or resting sites? Do they actually strike each other when they fight, or do they just bluff and try to scare the other ones away? Describe and/or draw a picture of two gulls fighting. Do they gulls make any noises while they are at your site? Describe them. Are some calls given more often than others? Do the gulls stand in any special positions when they give their calls? Describe and/or draw a picture of these positions. When the gulls move from place to place at your site, how do they move? Do they walk, hop, run, make short flights?

Markings and Adaptations

LUCY GAGLIARDO

5. *Markings and Adaptations:*
   Do all of the gulls on the site look the same? Why might some of them be different colors or sizes? Look at the birds' feet and/or find some gull tracks in the mud and think about the different places where the gull uses that foot to swim, walk, stand on the rocks, even perch in trees. What special things about the gulls feet help them do these things? Look at the gulls' beaks and watch how they use them for feeding, preening their feathers, or fighting Can you think of any tools that people use that are like the gull's beak? Look for feathers on your site which the gulls have dropped as they get new feathers. Look at the shape of the feathers and try to figure out what job they do and what part of the bird they came from.

Further Research: Take your students to the library and help them find books about gulls. Ask them to think of some good questions to ask their classmates.

Activity 3: Watching Waterbirds, Such as Ducks, Herons, and Egrets

Objective: To spend some time watching common waterbirds in a nearby park, lake, oceanfront.
Time: One period or more.

Methods: The same as above. Things to look for:

1. *General Description*
   How big is the bird? What is the shape of the bird? What is the size and shape of the bird's bill? What type of legs and feet does the bird have? What colors can you see on the bird? Is the bird alone or with other birds?
2. *Location*
   Is your bird: Swimming in the water? Flying over the water? Wading in shallow water? Walking, standing, or sitting on land?
3. *Flight*
   Describe how your bird flies. Draw a line to show the way your bird flies. Does your bird stop to hover in one place? Does your bird make dives down into the water from the air? If so, can you see any type of food being captured? Is your bird flying alone or with other birds of the same type? If it is flying with other birds, do they fly in any special pattern?
4. *Swimming*
   Does your bird dive underwater? How often does it dive? How long does it stay underwater? Does your bird come back up from its dive in the same spot or does it move to a new spot? Can you see if your bird is coming to the surface with any type of food in its mouth? If your bird does not dive, does it seem to be feeding at the surface or underwater by sticking its head and neck into the water?
5. *Activity on the shore*
   If your bird is moving, describe how it moves: runs, walks, waddles, hops, wades, etc. Does your bird seem to be searching for food? If it is searching, how does the bird use its bill (picking at the surface of sand or mud, probing in mud or sand, striking at small animals in shallow water, etc.)? Do other birds try to steal food from your bird, or chase it away from its feeding spot? Does your bird try to fight back or escape? What other observations can you make?

Activity 4: Drawing Birds

Objective: To give students experience, guidance, and confidence in learning how to draw birds.

Time: One period or more.

Materials: Drawing paper
Pencils
Stuffed birds or a place to view live birds

Method: Follow the steps outlined in the illustration as a way of progressing from the simple act of drawing circles to actually creating a life-like bird. Start your field sketch with an oval that approximates the general proportions of the bird. Regardless of whether you

Drawing a Bird

LUCY GAGLIARDO

intend to sketch an owl, heron, or robin, they all have oval (egg-shaped) bodies. It is the differences in wings, tails, and legs that give each species a distinctive form. Watch carefully to see at what angle the bird holds its body, then begin to assemble body parts, outlining head and neck, wings, tail, and legs. Concern yourself with proportions of the different parts to one another and the position of attachment, always referring to the living bird.

Drawing a Bird

Draw with smooth, flowing lines to achieve an outline sketch of the bird. Don't worry about erasing mistakes or lines you don't like. The goal should be to capture shape and posture with as few lines as possible before the bird flies away. Portray most behaviors by changing the posture of the bird's body (position of the oval) and the position of its appendages. If you see an unusual bird or one you can't identify, quickly draw a standard perching posture and then add details to illustrate distinctive field marks, carefully noting these in the margins of the page. Sketch birds in your field notebook or in a small artist's spiral sketchbook using a soft HB pencil, adding finer details with a harder pencil, such as a 4H. An art-gum eraser is useful for cleaning up sketches, but erasures should be kept to a minimum. Practive by sketching tame birds, such as captive parakeets, pigeons, or feeder birds. Sitting postures are easiest, but it won't take long before a few pencil lines will also capture the movement of birds in flight.

Activity 5: Project PigeonWatch

The Bird Education Department at the Cornell Laboratory of Ornithology has developed a nationwide research project in which schoolchildren observe and collect data about flocks of pigeons. Students search for color patterns, different types of behavior, etc. Their work helps scientists understand why pigeons of so many different colors exist in cities, while in the wild they look alike. Students send their completed data forms into the lab's office in Ithaca, New York, and receive summaries of the overall findings. Write to Project PigeonWatch, Cornell Lab of Ornithology, 159 Sapsucker Woods Road, Ithaca, NY 14850, or call (607) 254-2440

Activity 6: Project FeederWatch

This is another of the Cornell Laboratory of Ornithology's citizen science research projects supported by observations from thousands of individuals and hundreds of classes. Participants look at the variety of species making feeder visits, frequency of visits, and other variables. Classes collect information by watching their feeders for specific periods of time and send in their findings. Some of the discoveries already made include the fact that the dark-eyed junco is the most widespread bird at North American feeders, and that house sparrows are declining in many areas while house finches are increasing. Students receive quarterly summaries of what patterns are emerging. The Lab also offers ideas for different educational activities. Write or call the same address as above. In Canada contact: Bird Studies Canada/PFW, P.O. Box 160, Port Rowan, Ontario NOE 1MO, Canada.

Other Activities:

- Observing how birds make seed preferences at bird feeders is an easy and fun activity. You can put out dishes of oil sunflower seeds and striped sunflower seeds and see which type birds (such as chickadees and titmice) prefer. You can do the same for ground-feeding birds such as juncos and sparrows and experiment with different kinds of milo, millet, cracked corn, etc.
- Other bird feeder observations: Spend five minutes each hour, several days a week, counting the different species and how many of each type are visiting the feeders. This makes for good graphing data. You can also compare the activity of ground-level feeders with mid-level and high-level feeders, as well as the attraction values of various bird feeder designs. There are number of easy ways for school kids to make feeders from soda bottles, etc. Check bibliography.
- Build a 3x3-foot portable blind from burlap and 2x2s. Staple burlap to the frame and place a small chair or bench inside as an observation post. This can be stationed near a feeder, or a marsh or pond—someplace where the birds are active. Or, perhaps you can cut holes in the side of an old wooden building, shed, or garage and place a feeding station just outside.
- Make decoys and see what happens. Try building or buying (at a hardware or garden store) a lifesize replica of a Great Horned Owl and see if songbirds mob it during late spring and early summer. (Don't, however, keep it outside except during your experiment time because it could disrupt birdlife in the area.) This can be combined with sound; try playing a loop tape of horned owl calls in conjunction with the decoy. Other decoys you can try are floating ducks and geese.
- Graph actual data collected by Project Puffin. For example: the number of puffin chicks translocated each year, the number of those who survived four weeks of life on Eastern Egg Rock and who fledged (left for life at sea), and the number of puffins that came back to Eastern Egg Rock as adults or sub-adults. (These figures show how difficult it was to finally get enough puffins to actually re-establish a self-sustaining colony. You might want to theorize about what happened to all the missing chicks.)

Year	*Translocated*	*Fledged*	*Returned*
1973	6	5	0
1974	54	54	0
1975	94	91	8
1976	100	98	9
1977	100	99	56
1978	100	91	23
1979	100	92	26
1980	100	100	16
1981	100	100	16

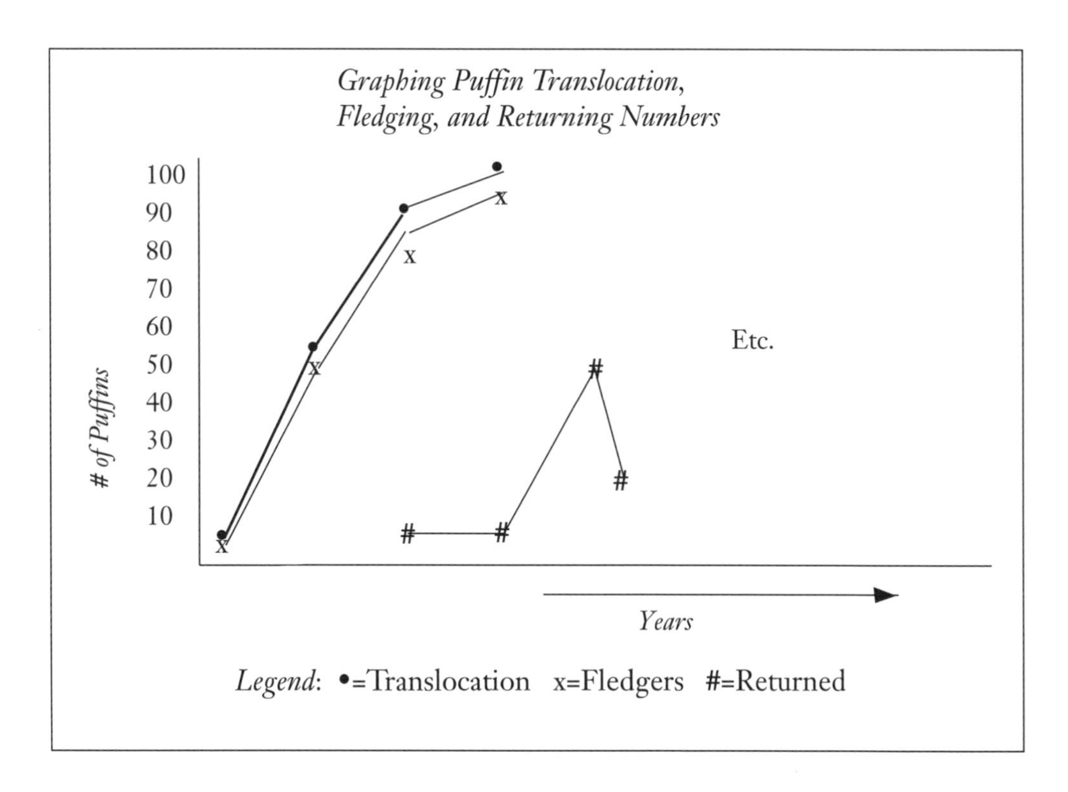

Bibliography

Adult Books:

Erickson, Laura. *Sharing the Wonder of Birds with Kids*. Pfeifer-Hamilton, 1997. Many good ideas, including a chapter called "Helping Kids Save Birds."

Graham Jr., Frank. *Gulls, a Social History*. Random House, 1975. A fascinating study of gulls and humans, with emphasis on New England. Black and white photos.

Hunken, Jorie. *Birdwatching For All Ages.* Globe Pequot, 1991. An excellent and comprehensive activity guide for adults working with children.

Internet Resources:

Backyard Bird Feeding
http://www.fws.gov/~r9mbmo/pamphlet/feed.html/#2

Becoming a Birdwatcher
http://www.nceet.snre.umich.edu/Curriculum/extra.html

Project PigeonWatch
http://www.ornith.cornell.edu/CS/PPW/main.html

Project FeederWatch
http://www.ornith.cornell.edu/CS/PFW/main.html

Classroom FeederWatch
http://www.ornith.cornell.edu/CS/CFW/main.html

Also see the general Internet resources on birds on pages 4–6.

Theme VI: One Person With a Dream Can Make a Difference

Introduction

When Project Puffin first began in 1973, Steve Kress was working as an ornithology instructor at National Audubon Society's Ecology Camp in Maine, on Hog Island. Every two weeks each summer about fifty adults came to the large, spruce-covered island to learn about nature, and to live in a pristine environment where tides and weather ruled each day. A tremendous sense of peace and the feeling of being part of the natural world seemed to gently find its way into everyone lucky enough to spend time there. There was also an effort on the part of some staff members to build up an awareness, and perhaps a sense of responsibility, to the Todd and Bingham families who had saved the island from being sold and lumbered just after the turn of the century, and who had interested the National Audubon Society in opening up a camp for youth leaders and teachers. Much of Steve Kress's inspiration for conceiving the idea that a puffin colony could be restored came from seeing what a fine center of learning Hog Island had become.

The camp experience, which continues today for both adults and children, only exists because of what the Todds, the Binghams, and others did and continue to do. The currents of hope and inspiration which have emanated from that island since the camp opened in 1936 are a continuing testimony to the power of a great idea, and how a few dedicated and caring people can achieve great things.

Those of us working with young people know how important it is to give encouragement to their ideas, and to help them along in believing in themselves and their abilities to shape their worlds. The children you work with may not know a finch from a femur, but they can make an impact, especially in their own neighborhoods, homes, and schools. What follows are several activities designed to inspire both thought and action.

Note: Theme VII gets more into the nuts and bolts of school projects such as habitat improvement, building birdhouses, etc. The activities in this section are focused more on building inspiration and ideas.

Activity 1: Inspiring Personalities

Objective: To motivate and encourage children by sharing with them stories of what other people have done.

Time: One period or less.

Methods: The following brief stories portray several individuals who decided to follow their imagination in order to accomplish a specific goal. Read several to your students to get them thinking about their own potential contributions to the earth and its inhabitants. Discussion questions are at the end of this section.

John James Audubon (1785–1851)

When John James Audubon was eighteen years old his father, a sea captain, sent him from France to America. The year was 1803. John James had not done well in school, and he had flunked out of the French naval academy. His father thought his son could help manage a farm he had bought in Pennsylvania. But John James wasn't interested in responsibility. He wanted to play and lead a carefree life. And he wanted to study birds and nature, something he had done as a child back in France.

When Audubon reached the new world of America, he found it filled with exciting opportunities to see birds, animals and plants he had never seen before. Audubon began drawing the birds he saw but he wasn't pleased with his work. He thought his drawings were stiff and lifeless. He began shooting birds, like many early bird-watchers did, and then stuffing them and putting wires inside their bodies so they'd be in a lifelike pose. Audubon's hope was to draw birds as if they were alive, and not as if they were a dead corpse.

Audubon was a friendly man, popular with his neighbors, and soon he married an attractive woman named Lucy. They moved to Kentucky where he owned and operated a general store. But he was not a very good businessman, and over the years he went from one job to another. He even painted people's portraits when he needed money, which was often. He remained inspired, however, and was continually fascinated by birds. So fascinated that one day he decided he would try to do the impossible—he would draw and paint every bird specie in eastern North America! In today's world that would be difficult, even with our cars and planes and fine binoculars and cameras. Imagine what it must have been like nearly two hundred years ago!

Audubon travelled by horseback, stagecoach, boat, and by foot to the far reaches of wild America, carrying his paints and papers with him. He worked for years, often leaving his wife and family far behind. He camped with Native Americans, trappers, and woodsmen. He fought off storms, biting insects, and hunger. But he eventually succeeded, creating 435 different prints, each one measuring about 30 by 40 inches. This was called his "Elephant Folio" because it was so big in size.

Audubon went on to write a five-volume set of books about the birds he had painted. But it was his art that made him famous. His lively paintings of birds became well known throughout America and Europe. Many people wanted to buy copies of these paintings, and Audubon was finally making money. His years of hard work, trying and trying again had succeeded. He had captured the beauty and life of his subjects.

Audubon's paintings are still seen today in many books and museums. And more than half a million people around the country are members of the National Audubon Society, which works hard to save animals, plants, and habitats. Now you know where the name for the Audubon societies came from. Have you seen Audubon's artwork? Are you familiar with what an Audubon society is doing in your area?

Rachel Carson (1907–1964)

As a young girl Rachel Carson grew up with her family in a house alongside the Allegheny River in Pennsylvania. She spent much of her childhood exploring the nearby woods and riverbanks. She also loved to write, and when she was eleven years old, incredibly enough, a magazine published a fictional story of hers.

She went to college with the idea of becoming a full-time writer, but changed her mind when she took her first biology class. Taught by a woman who was later to become her good friend and guide, the class ignited her passion for studying science. Rachel continued to write, spending most of her time learning how the earth's living creatures and plants survive. Upon graduating from college she went to Cape Cod, Massachusetts, for a summer job studying ocean life. The time she spent near the sea was a turning point in Rachel's life.

Have you ever stopped along a beach to look at the interesting things that have washed up, or poked around and under the rocks for starfish and crabs? Rachel loved doing that, too, and she decided to make the study of the sea her life's work. She combined her writing talents with her knowledge of the ocean and for many years worked for the U.S. Fish and Wildlife Service, writing and editing scientific articles and booklets.

In the 1940s she wrote her first book, *Under The Sea Wind*. She followed it up in the 1950s with *The Sea Around Us*, a book that became very popular and was made into a movie. In it she wrote about the mysteries and wonders of ocean creatures.

In the late 1950s a friend sent her a newspaper clipping describing how birds were being killed by a chemical that farmers sprayed on their crops to kill insects. Rachel began studying the effects of these chemicals (pesticides) and soon realized it was a terrible problem. The pesticides were making their way into the bodies of many other animals who lived in the spraying area. For example, fish in streams got poisoned when the chemicals washed off the crops in a rainstorm. Then birds that ate fish, such as eagles, got it into their bodies.

Rachel spent four years writing a book about these things. She called it *Silent Spring*. Can you guess what that title refers to? Imagine an April or May morning without any birds singing! This was Rachel's worry.

Her book became very popular, and even President John Kennedy was concerned about the problems Rachel described. Many other people were sad and angry about the uncontrolled use of these dangerous chemicals, and within a few years the U.S. Congress passed laws stopping the use of some of the worst pesticides. Rachel Carson told the nation about a dangerous threat to the environment, and even though the chemical companies tried to make her look bad, people woke up and did something about it. Thanks to Rachel Carson we do not have a silent spring!

Kevin Bell (1978–)

When Kevin was twelve years old he was encouraged by a teacher to enter the Nevada State Science Fair. Kevin came up with the general idea of testing water for impurities, but wasn't sure exactly what he was going to do. He found out that wildlife at a nearby National Wildlife Refuge were dying, so he went there, talked to several workers, and took home samples of agricultural waters that drained into the refuge.

He tried to grow beans in it but none grew. He put a variety of small animals (snails, fish, daphnia) in the water, but they all soon died. He added fresh water to his samples and the second group of animals lived longer. He continued to conduct his tests for two and a half months. He organized a display, entered it in the science fair, and won first prize!

Kevin's project was written up in newspapers. Officials at the National Wildlife Refuge looked over his notebooks, and passed them on to people in Washington at the Interior Department. The Senator from Nevada used Kevin's work to write a law that was passed by Congress. The contaminated drain was closed. Then the local office of The Nature Conservancy purchased fresh water to add to the partially contaminated water in the refuge. Kevin was there to help open the floodgates. He eventually met President Bush, and is now working on other ways to clean up polluted waters.

General Discussion Questions:
What are some common themes that run through each of the biographies? How would you describe some of the qualities of each personality? Why do you think each person was able to accomplish what he or she did? Is it reasonable to think that you or someone in your class could also do similar things?

Activity 2: Local Heroes

Objective: For students to find out who some local or regional environmental activists are, and to interview them.

Time: Varies.

Methods: Find out the names of people in your area who are active in environmental causes such as land protection, restoration, wildlife issues, solid waste, etc., and ask if they will come to talk to your class. Students can prepare questions and write up an interview or a short biography. They can design or create visual aids or displays which illustrate the person's work.

Locate local eco-heroes by contacting local chapters of the Audubon Society, and other environmental groups such as Sierra Club, Nature Conservancy, Greenpeace, etc.

Activity 3: Dreaming Your Dream

Objective: Using the techniques of guided imagery and creative writing, give students the opportunity to think of things they'd like to accomplish.

Setting: Classroom. Sit in chairs or on a rug.

Time: Five to ten minutes for the exercise, ten to twenty minutes for followup.

Materials: Paper and pens
Painting or drawing materials

Methods: Set the scene for a guided imagery. If you've never done this before, tell the children you'd like them to really use their imaginations for the following challenge. Set the ground rules by asking for no talking and no interrupting anyone else. As students sit quietly with their eyes closed or focused softly on a spot on the floor, tell them you're going to present them with opportunities to do something positive for animals, for plants, and for people. (You may choose to do one each day rather than in one sitting.) Start the activity by asking them to take several deep and slow breaths. Ignore any giggling if it's not too bothersome—it should stop.

Say, "Think of the earth as it looks from outer space—the blue oceans, the white clouds, the dark land masses. Pretend you can glide down to take a closer look. You're swooping lower and lower. You can see great areas of deserts, mountains, and lakes. As you get closer you can see all kinds of different animals. Some of you might be over the arctic, some might be over the rainforests, some above little ponds or over the ocean. You see many different kinds of animals. Let your eyes sweep over the habitat. Some of you might see some problems. Some of the animals you see may be in trouble. Go help an animal in trouble."
(Pause for one minute).

"Now it's time to come back. Feel yourself lifting upwards, away from the place you've been, back to our classroom. I'm going to count to ten. Count with me when I reach six and then open your eyes at number ten. You'll feel alert and will remember all the details of your journey. One...two...three...."

(At a different time consider trying a similar approach to plants, and to fellow humans.)

Debriefing: Talk about what came up—what they saw, how their bodies felt, etc. Then give students time to write, draw, or paint. As author Maureen Murdock says in her book, *Spinning Inward*, "Go slowly at first and respect everyone's timing. Children are much closer to their inner images than we adults are. Allow them their own time to reveal their experiences to you. You can't force an orchid to bloom; you can, however, delight in the process of unfolding."

Or, instead of guided imageries, put the following questions up on the board:

- If you could do something "significant," (within the categories of helping the earth, the animals, the plants, and humans) what would it be?
- How would you do it?
- What problems might you run into?
- How would you get help?
- How would you convince others of the need to take action?
- What might be the end results of success?
- What needs to be done in your town? In your school? In America?
- Who is already doing good things in your home, school, town, etc?
- Can you get involved with them?

Give students enough time to write "essays" about these possibilities. Perhaps do one subject area each, or one each day for three days, etc. Have children share their ideas. Decide where to go from there. Are there ways to actually accomplish any of these things? (This ties in with Theme VII.)

Activity 4: Making an Environmental Pledge

Objective: To become aware of our own environmental "bad" habits and to correct them with new behaviors.

Time: One-half to one period.

Materials: 3x5-inch file cards
Pens

Setting: Classroom, etc.

Methods: Begin with a short personal anecdote such as: "As I was brushing my teeth this morning, I looked down into the sink and realized, 'My goodness, the water is running!' I was standing there, brushing my teeth and all this water was just running down the drain, for no reason at all. It occurred to me that maybe thousands or even millions of people were doing the same thing, or maybe worse things, like pouring waste oil into the ground or throwing plastics into the ocean. Imagine how good it would be if people started changing their environmental bad habits. I wonder if people in this classroom might take a moment to think about their environmental bad habits."

Open the floor to discussion. After a number of students share their stories, announce that most people seem to have some environmental bad habits so you're going to be passing out (two) file cards to each person. (See diagram for layout.) Each student will write down his or

Environmental Pledge Card

Name ______________________________	Date: __________
My environmental bad habit is: ______________________________	
______________________________	
My environmental pledge is: ______________________________	
______________________________	
I will begin on: ______________________________	
Signature: ______________________________	
Witness: ______________________________	

her name, the date, his or her environmental bad habit, an environmental pledge, and the day he or she will start. Each card will be signed. The student will keep one card for him or herself, and one will be passed to the teacher who will keep them as a record.

Give students time to do this. Collect one of the cards from each student. Resume discussion by asking if they'd like to share their bad habits and their pledges.

Check back the next day to see how folks did with their pledges. Check for several more days, then again in a week and again in a month, etc. Have students share stories of success, failure, effect on siblings, parents, etc.

Supplemental Activity: If an environmental pledge works for an individual, what might happen if you decide as a class to do the same? For example, are there signs of waste on a community-wide basis? You might want to tackle a recycling system, a clean-up, a pledge to feed birds, etc.

Bibliography

Kids Books:

Anderson, Joan, *Earth Keepers*. Harcourt Brace, 1993. Portrays three environmental groups and the work they do.

Cherry, Lynne. *A River Ran Wild*. Harcourt Brace, 1992. A beautifully illustrated story about a river in New Hampshire, from wilderness times to modern days. Focuses on successful efforts to restore the river back to health.

Earthworks Group. *Kid Heroes of the Environment*. Earthworks Group, 1995. A heartwarming and useful little paperback which portrays several dozen kids and groups who have done something positive for the earth. Gives simple step-by-step advice for replicating each individual's project, as well as resource information.

Faber, Doris and Harold. *Great Lives; Nature and the Environment*. Scribner's Sons, 1991. Twenty-six biographies, including those of Rachel Carson, Thoreau, John Burroughs, Aldo Leopold, and Charles Darwin. About twelve pages on each person, with photos.

Lewis, Barbara. *Kids With Courage*. Free Spirit Publishing, 1992. The story of Kevin Bell came from this volume. For older children.

McMillan, Bruce. *Night of the Pufflings*. Houghton Mifflin, 1995. Shows how children on the Icelandic isle of Heimaey rescue fledgling puffins who get lost on their way to the ocean from their burrows. Excellent photographs.

Peavy, Linda and Smith, Ursula. *Dreams into Deeds: Nine Women Who Dared*. Scribners, 1985. Nine well-written portraits of accomplished women, including Rachel Carson. Photos. A bit more informational and for a slightly older audience than *Living Dangerously*.

Rappaport, Doreen. *Living Dangerously: American Women Who Risked Their Lives for Adventure*. Harper Collins, 1991. Six exciting portraits of female adventurers, including one of Dr. Eugenie Clark, a diver/marine scientist. Inspiring.

Rose, Deborah Lee. *The People Who Hugged The Trees*. Roberts Rinehart, 1990. An inspiring story, based on fact, about a village that fought to save its forest from a greedy Maharajah.

Sirch, Willow Ann. *Eco-Women: Protectors of the Earth*. Fulcrum Publishing, 1996. Biographies of eight women, with photos and suggestions for action. Nicely done.

Adult Books:

Fradin, Dennis. *Remarkable Children*. Little, Brown, 1987. An intriguing compendium of short biographies of some famous people in their earlier years.

Keene, Ann T., *Observers and Protectors of Nature*. Oxford University Press, 1994. Portraits of 100 American conservationists, from past to present. Well done, good photos.

McKibben, Bill. *Hope, Human and Wild: True Stories of Living Lightly on the Earth*. Little, Brown, 1995.

Murdock, Maureen. *Spinning Inward; Using Guided Imagery with Children for Learning, Creativity, and Relaxation*. Shambhala Publishers, 1988. Gives details of the why and how of guided imagery.

Steidl, Kim Sakamoto, *Environmental Portraits: People Making a Difference for the Environment*. Good Apple, 1993. With a chronological and comprehensive series of interesting profiles as the core material, the author has developed discussion questions and projects relevant to many aspects of environmental issues. In handy workbook structure, for fourth to sixth graders.

Wallace, Aubrey. *Green Means: Living Gently on the Planet*. KQED (San Francisco) Books and Tapes, 1994. Based on the popular PBS television spots, this book portrays 20 success stories of local environmental activists. The original video is also available.

Internet Resources:

Audubon's Birds of America (art and full text of his books)
http://quality.cqs.ch/~rrb/Audubon/

"Children and Nature," by Rachel Carson
http://www.bruderhof.org/ploughs/plough48/nature.htm

Also see the Internet listings for environmental organizations on pages 67–68.

Theme VII: Projects to Help or Restore Animals, Plants, and Habitats Are Taking Place Around the World

Introduction

We began translocating puffin chicks from Canada to the coast of Maine in 1973. At the time, the concept of "restoration ecology" was a fairly new idea. What scientists around the world are now attempting to do with increasing frequency is to bring back or restore animals to places they once inhabited.

This technique has promise if the habitat is intact. We were fortunate that Eastern Egg Rock was still a wild island, surrounded by areas rich in fish species. In many other cases, habitat has been badly degraded, or totally lost. For example, how could you restore salmon to a river if a dam or a number of dams blocked access to their spawning grounds? How could you lure Least Terns and Piping Plovers to a proposed nesting beach if dune buggies and dogs have free run?

A few examples of successful animal restoration projects through translocation are timber wolves in Wyoming and Idaho, Bald Eagles in New York, Peregrine Falcons and wild turkeys in various eastern states, and Black-footed Ferrets in Wyoming.

Translocation, however, is just one strategy. In cases where animals and habitat are still surviving, people are working to help in a variety of ways. Some examples are protection of sea turtle nesting beaches in Latin America and the southern U.S. from poachers, the planting of flowers, trees, and fruiting shrubs as wildlife food sources, and the building and maintenance of bluebird boxes and wood duck boxes through various parts of America. Much can be done locally by your students. What follows are projects you may want to begin at your school, as well as brief summaries of more formal wildlife projects, and where to write or call for more information.

Activity 1: School Activities

The proverb "Think globally, act locally" is, we believe, a wise one. Consider your school grounds. You can set up bird feeding stations (see previous theme for activities), or perhaps you can work with the managers of a local park so that your students can help plant vegetation beneficial to wildlife, pull exotic vegetation, put up birdhouses, etc.

Suburban and rural schools offer more outside possibilities, but even inner city schools have a variety of choices such as Project Pigeon Watch, etc. What follows are some ideas you might consider:

- Survey your school grounds with the help of a local expert (garden club, local park, Audubon group, etc.) to identify unique habitat, such as a vernal pool that may need protection, or places where you can plant beneficial vegetation or erect birdhouses. Project Wild, a national teacher training and curriculum development organization, has recently created a program designed for this very purpose called "Wild School Sites." Write to Project Wild at 4014

Chatham Lane, Houston, TX 77027. The New Hampshire Fish and Game Department has also produced an excellent action guide entitled *Homes For Wildlife: A Planning Guide For Habitat Enhancement on School Grounds*. It's available for $10 from the Department at 2 Hazen Drive, Concord, NH 03301, or by calling (603) 271-3211.

• Use the services of your shop teacher or custodians for access to tools and lumber with which to build birdhouses, and bird-nesting platforms (for barn owls, geese, loons, osprey, etc.). There are many books and pamphlets containing plans, including the one just noted from the New Hampshire Fish and Game Department. Look in the nature section of a good bookstore, a nature center gift shop, or find plans through your local 4-H or Cooperative Extension Office. Also, the Minnesota Department of Natural Resources has written a book entitled *Woodworking for Wildlife*, which includes plans and diagrams for 24 projects. Contact them at 500 Lafayette Road, Box 7, Centennial Building, St. Paul, MN 55155-4007.

• Are there places where you can cut or pull invasive vegetation such as purple loosestrife, phragmites, and multi-flora rose? Where are good places to plant native species of flowers, ferns, and shrubs? The Minnesota Department of Natural Resources has another fine book, *Landscaping For Wildlife*, available at the above address.

• If there's a stream on or near your property, you may want to become local researchers and protectors. The Izaak Walton League has a national program called "Save our Streams" which includes a variety of scientific and educational activities. You'll find out what lives where, and how to measure the health of local streams. Kids become local "wardens." Izaak Walton League, 1401 Wilson Blvd. Arlington, VA 22209.

• Vernal pools are small woodland pools that usually fill up with water for three seasons but are dry during the summers. They furnish extremely important habitat for the breeding of wood frogs, spotted salamanders, fairy shrimp, and other delicate species. The state of Massachusetts has pioneered the identification and protection of vernal pools. Threats to these ephemeral jewels include road salt, toxic runoff, draining, acid rain, and development. Search your property or a nearby preserve for vernal pools and get your students involved. Vernal Pool Association, Reading Memorial High School, 62 Oakland Rd., Reading, MA 01867.

• A bluebird trail. Bluebirds are magnificent little birds that have lost much of their nesting habitat—hollow trees and rotting fenceposts—during decades of clearing and the use of metal fences. Introduced species, such as starlings and house sparrows, have also pushed them out. If there is cleared land near you, such as meadows, pastures, or even athletic fields that are bordered by some woods, you may have good bluebird habitat! Plans to build these boxes are readily available (see above references). Students can even do arithmetic projects by graphing how many boxes are used, how many eggs are laid, chicks hatched, chicks fledged, clutches laid each season, etc. Ask for help in identifying the right habitat. A local lumberyard might donate the wood you need. A good resource is the North American Bluebird Society, P.O. Box 6295, Silver Spring, MD 20906. (Also see bibliography.)

• Build brush piles. Small mammals such as rabbits, opossums, raccoons, and weasels will benefit from brush piles. Use stumps and logs for the foundation; they allow air spaces to be created once you cover them with brush and branches.

- Adopt-A-Species. A wonderfully successful program from California encourages classes and entire schools to consider "adopting" an endangered or threatened plant or animal. Teachers and students pick a species, learn about it, develop a plan of action, educate the wider community, and then take steps to protect the organism or habitat.

One fourth grade class in San Anselmo helped rescue endangered freshwater shrimp by cleaning up and restoring creekside areas upstream from the shrimp's habitat. They also convinced local cattle ranchers to keep their stock away from certain areas of the stream where the shrimp live. They held public meetings, wrote letters, published a newsletter, designed t-shirts, and raised money.

For more information about this empowering program, which is sponsored by two California state agencies and the National Audubon Society, write to: National Audubon Society, 376 Greenwoood Beach Road, Tiburon, CA 94920, or call (415) 388-2524. Project directors have prepared a teacher's guide which may be ordered for $6 from the California Department of Education Sales Unit, P.O. Box 271, Sacramento, CA 95812-0271.

Activity 2: Brief Summaries of Several Major Wildlife Projects and How to Find Out More.

Restoration of Wolves to Yellowstone National Park and Idaho

In the winter of 1994–1995 the U.S. Fish and Wildlife Service began its first translocation of Canadian wolves to former wolf habitat in Wyoming and Idaho. A second group was re-introduced into the same territory during the following winter. This is one of the most interesting and controversial wildlife projects in the United States because it deals with a top-of-the-food-chain predator that is feared and misunderstood by many people. Biologists continue to face a barrage of legal and emotional roadblocks to their plan, and a translocated wolf has already been shot. But wolves are a key member of the Yellowstone/Rocky Mountain bio-regions for many reasons, and their re-appearance after a long and sad history of extermination has inspired many citizens. For more information write to the U.S. Fish and Wildlife Service, Publications Unit, 4040 N. Fairfax Drive, Arlington, VA 22203, or call (703) 358-2504. Also check the *Reader's Guide to Periodical Literature* or the *New York Times Index*.

Other resource groups include: Alliance for the Wild Rockies, P.O. Box 8731, Missoula, MT. 59807. The Predator Project, P.O. Box 6733, Bozeman, MT. 59771. Wolf Recovery Foundation, P.O. Box 793, Boise, ID 83701. A good children's book on this subject is *When the Wolves Return* by Thomas Mangelsen, Cobblehill, 1995.

Re-Introduction of the Black-Footed Ferret to Wyoming

These attractive little members of the weasel family are America's most endangered mammal. They were thought to be extinct, but a small colony was discovered in 1981 in their typical habitat—a prairie dog town—in Wyoming. Ferrets had disappeared as prairies were settled, and as prairie dogs were poisoned by ranchers concerned their livestock would break legs by stepping in prairie dog holes. Several black-footed ferrets in the previously unknown location were live-trapped and a captive breeding program was started by the U.S. Fish and Wildlife Service and the Wyoming Game and Fish Department. In 1991 the first release of 49 ferrets back to the wild took place, again in Wyoming. Other releases and studies have followed. For information, contact the Fish and Wildlife Service at the above address.

Restoration of Peregrine Falcons

When the Peregrine Falcon was teetering on the brink of extinction because of pesticides in its food supply, a Cornell professor named Tom Cade decided to try something no one had ever done before: raise the magnificent raptors in captivity and re-introduce young ones to former breeding areas (remote cliffs). Dr. Cade succeeded beyond his wildest dreams; more than 4,000 peregrines have been released in 28 states since the program began in the early 1970s. The Peregrine Fund is also working with other birds of prey such as eagles, kestrels, tropical raptors, and the California Condor. It has an active education department as well as a visitor's center. For more information write to The Peregrine Fund, 5666 West Flying Hawk Lane, Boise, ID 83709, or call (208) 362-3716.

California Condors—Will They Survive?

The population of these huge scavengers was reduced over past centuries by hunting and inadvertent poisoning to a total of 20–25 birds, all living in the mountains of southern California. In the early 1980s, the U.S. Fish and Wildlife Service, the National Audubon Society, and other agencies came up with a complex rescue plan that seemed likely to fail because of the extraordinarily low remaining numbers, the very slow reproduction cycle, and other factors. But persistence and lots of effort are beginning to pay off. The population has grown to more than 80 birds through captive breeding at three different western centers, and birds are being slowly released into the wild. For more information about this heartening program, contact the U.S. Fish and Wildlife Service at the above address, or the Peregrine Fund (one of the captive breeding sites).

Bibliography

Kids Books:

Brooks, Felicity. *Protecting Endangered Species*. Usborne/EDC Publishing, 1991. A colorful little paperback filled with information.

Cone, Molly, *Come Back Salmon: How a Group of Dedicated Kids Adopted Pigeon Creek and Brought It Back to Life*. Sierra Club and Little, Brown, 1992. Describes the efforts of an elementary school in Washington to clean up a nearby stream, stock it with salmon, and preserve it as an unpolluted place where the salmon could return.

Earthworks Group. *50 Simple Things Kids Can Do to Save the Earth*. Earthworks Group, 1990. Practical hands-on activities and advice.

Gay, Kathlyn. *Caretakers of the Earth*. Enslow, 1993. (For older kids.)

Grolier Education Corporation. *Grolier Student Encyclopedia of Endangered Species*. 1995. An informative and global view, ten volumes.

Holmes, Anita. *I Can Save The Earth*. Julian Messner/Simon and Shuster. 1993

National Geographic. *Wildlife Making A Comeback*. National Geographic Books, 1987. Lots of good photos and text on global wildlife stories.

Schorsch, Nancy. *Saving The Condor*. Franklin Watts, 1991. Describes the life history of the condor and the rescue project.

Adult Books:

Berger, John. *Restoring The Earth*. Knopf, 1985, Doubleday Anchor 1987. Detailed and interesting stories of people involved in grassroots restoration work, from planting trees and reclaiming rivers to the solarization of a small town.

Dunlap, Thomas. *Saving America's Wildlife*. Princeton University Press, 1986. A scholarly discussion of American attitudes towards wildlife during the last hundred years.

Mills, Stephanie. *In Service of the Wild: Restoring and Re-inhabiting Damaged Land*. Beacon Press, 1995

New Hampshire Fish and Game Department. *Homes For Wildlife*. 1993. Good ideas for on-site school projects.

North American Bluebird Society. *Getting To Know Bluebirds!*, an educational package for use in grades four through six. Available from the North American Bluebird Society, P.O. Box 6295, Silver Springs, MD 20916.

Ortho Books. *Building Birdhouses and Feeders*. 1990. Excellent plans and illustrations.

Project Wild. *Wild School Sites: Project Wild*, 1993. Details hands-on projects for improving school grounds for wildlife.

Stokes, Donald and Lillian. *The Birdfeeder Book*. Little, Brown, 1987. Very easy to understand, well done.

Stokes, Donald and Lillian. *The Complete Birdhouse Book*. Little, Brown, 1990. Also excellent.

Stokes, Donald and Lillian. *The Bluebird Book*. Little, Brown, 1991. A comprehensive look at the bluebird's life, and how to attract the bird and house it.

U.S. Department of the Interior. *Restoring America's Wildlife*. A detailed look at 50 years of wildlife and habitat restoration undertaken by government agencies. Photos, illustrations, and information on more than 15 different managed species.

Yates, Steve. *Adopting A Stream: A Northwest Handbook*. University of Washington Press, 1988. Hands-on advice for adopting a stream. (Also see Izaak Walton League.)

Internet Resources:

See the Internet recources at the end of Theme III for information on wolves and other endangered animals.

North American Bluebird Society
Includes information about *Getting to Know Bluebirds!*, an educational package from the North American Bluebird Society.
http://ww.WSD.com/WSD/nabluebird

Izaak Walton League
Includes information on "The Stream Study"
http://iwla.org/iwla/

National Wildlife Federation
Information on Schoolyard Habitat programs, sample articles, quizzes, and games from *Ranger Rick* magazine.
http://www.igc.apc.org/nwf/

Environmental Defense Fund
Information on their programs, includes an Earth to Kids page.
http://www.edf.,org/heap/schoolindex/html

Air and Waste Management Association
Information on their Teacher Training Program, a section called "What Can You Do," with tips on recycling.
http://www.awma.org/pub.html

Environmental Organizations for Kids

Earth Force, 1501 Wilson Boulevard, Twelfth Floor, Arlington, VA 22209; (703) 243-7400. Launched in 1994 by a grant from the Pew Charitable Trust, this action-oriented group provides information to youth and encourages and supports their local initiatives. They sponsor Pennies for the Planet, whereby children raise money through the collection of pennies for environmental projects, such as migratory birds, forest protection, etc. They also sponsor national town meetings of youth speaking out for the earth, as well as colorful and creative campaigns for protecting trees, wildlife, etc. Web Page is http://www.igc.apc.org/earthforce/

The Natural Guard, 142 Howard Avenue, New Haven, CT. 06519; (203) 787-0229. Urban in focus, international in scope, they offer information, tools and mentoring needed to assess local communities' environmental needs.

Tree Musketeers, 136 Main Street, El Segundo, CA 90245; (800) 473-0263. Youth learn to be leaders in a group founded and run by kids; organizers of Youth Summits, community forestry programs, speakers bureau and hotline.

YMCA Earth Service Corps, National Headquarters, 909 4th Avenue,
Seattle, WA 98104; 800-733-YESC. From tree-planting to protecting watersheds, this group works with local school clubs all over the U.S.

Other Resources for Adults

Canadian Wildlife Federation, 2740 Queensview Dr., Ottawa, ON, K2B 1A2, Canada. Publications include *Your Big Backyard*, *Canadian Wildlife*, *Biosphere*, and *Ranger Rick*.
Center for Environmental Education, 400 Columbus Avenue, Valhalla, NY 10595; (914) 747-8200. Houses and distributes the nation's most comprehensive collection of environmental education materials. These can be browsed via an online service, or borrowed by mail. They also sponsor Green School's Peer Partners in Environmental Education Program, whereby high school students "adopt" an elementary school or class and hold monthly workshops.

National Audubon Society's Audubon Adventures, 613 Riversville Road, Greenwich, CT 06831. Every month a new nature topic is explored via a teacher's guide and newspaper magazines for students. The National Audubon Society's Web Page is at http://www.igc.apc.org/audubon/

National Audubon Society's Ecology Camps. Same address as above. Each summer the society operates adult camps in Maine, Connecticut, and Wyoming. One-week sessions; scholarships often available through local Audubon chapters and garden clubs. There are also two ten-day sessions for children ages 10 to 14 at the camp in Maine and at a new site in Vermont.

National Wildlife Federation, 8925 Leesburg Pike, Vienna, VA 22184; 800–477–5560. Publishes *Ranger Rick*, and the environmental education series *Animal Tracks*. Web Page is at http://www.nwf.org

Nature Conservancy, 1815 N. Lynn St., Arlington, VA 22209; 405–521–2293. Offers "Spirit of the Last Great Places" environmental education guide. Web Page at http://www.tnc.org/

North American Loon Fund, 6 Lily Pond Road, Gilford, NH 03246. Distributes information, a poster, and other resources regarding the protection, study, and restoration of these magnificent birds.

World Wildlife Fund of Canada, #504, 90 Eglinton Ave. E., Toronto, ON, M4P 2Z7, Canada. Publications include *Working for Wildlife* and *Schools for Wildlife*.

Aquariums and Zoos That House Live Puffins:

Baltimore Aquarium
Lincoln Park Zoo, Chicago
Cincinnati Zoo
Indianapolis Zoo
Montreal Biodome
New England Aquarium (exhibits scheduled to open November 1997)
Newport Oregon Coast Aquarium
New York Central Park Wildlife Center
New York Zoological Society Wildlife Center (Bronx Zoo)
North Carolina Zoological Park, Asheboro
Omaha Henry Doorly Zoo
St. Paul Como Zoo, Minnesota
Seattle Aquarium
Sea World of Florida, Orlando
Sea World of Texas, San Antonio
Sea World of California, San Diego

Puffin-Watching Boat Trips in Maine (June to August)

To Eastern Egg Rock:

From New Harbor: *Hardy Boat Cruises*, 1-800-2-Puffin. These daily trips usually run from early June to mid-August, and last about an hour and a half. Narrated by an Audubon educator.
From Boothbay Harbor: *Cap'n Fish, Inc.* (207) 633-3244. Trips go out about three times a week, from late June to early August, and take about three hours. Narrated by an Audubon educator.

To Matinicus Rock and Seal Island National Wildlife Refuge:

From Rockland: *Atlantic Expeditions*. (207) 372-8621. An all-day trip. Begins in early June and runs until mid-August. Narrated by an Audubon educator.

To Machias Seal Island:

From Jonesport: *Captains Barna and John Norton*. (207) 497-5933. A half-day trip to the largest puffin colony in the Gulf of Maine.
From Cutler: *Bold Coast Charter Company*. (207) 259-4484. Similar itinerary as above.

Adopt-A-Puffin

Project Puffin was established in 1973 to reintroduce Atlantic puffins to their former Maine coast nesting islands. You can help support our efforts by adopting your own puffin. For each $100 gift, we enroll you in our Adopt-A-Puffin program and assign one Atlantic puffin to you.

Each puffin was taken on a journey—over 1,000 miles by air, land, and sea—from Newfoundland to grow up on Eastern Egg Rock (as featured in our companion book *Project Puffin*). Adopt-A-Puffin is a great school fund-raising project because all of the money received goes directly to restoration efforts, and because the process can help to focus students' attention on learning more about these endearing birds.

Each enrollee in the program will receive a full-color photograph of their puffin, its individual biography from pre-fledging age to the most recent sightings, and a certificate of adoption signed by Dr. Stephen Kress.

To participate, write to: Project Puffin, 159 Sapsucker Woods Road, Ithaca, NY 14850.

The National Audubon Society

The mission of the National Audubon Society is to conserve and restore natural ecosystems, focusing on birds, other wildlife, and their habitats for the benefit of humanity and the earth's biological diversity.

A leader in the environmental movement,. Audubon has more than 560,000 members and more than 500 chapters, plus education and nature centers that welcome visitors. We also have a professional staff of scientists, lobbyists, lawyers, policy analysts, and educators.

Through our nationwide sanctuary system, we manage 150,000 acres of critical wildlife habitat and unique natural areas for birds, wild animals, and rare plant life.

Audubon magazine, published six times a year and sent to all members, carries outstanding articles and color photography on wildlife, nature, and environmental issues. We also publish *Audubon Adventures*, a natural history children's newsletter reaching 600,000 students in 20,000 classrooms.

Our acclaimed *World of Audubon* television documentaries on TBS deal with many environmental themes, while our children's series for The Disney Channel, *Audubon's Animals*, introduces families to endangered wildlife species.

Audubon sponsors books and electronic programs on nature, plus travel programs to exotic places like Antartica, Africa, Australia, Baja California, Galapagos Islands, Indonesia, and Patagonia.

For further information about any of Audubon's programs, please write or call:

National Audubon Society
700 Broadway
New York, NY 10003
800-813-5037
212-979-3000

Web Page at http://www.audubon.org/audubon